OVER THERE!

Stories of World War I

SELECTED BY
PHYLLIS R. FENNER

ILLUSTRATED BY
WILLIAM R. LOHSE

WILLIAM MORROW & COMPANY, INC.

© 1961

U. S. 1408180

"Over there, over there,
Send the word, send the word
Over there
That the Yanks are coming,
The Yanks are coming,
The drums rum-tum-ming everywhere."

On a quiet June day in 1914 an Austrian arch-duke was assassinated in a little Serbian town. Europe, just waiting for a pretext, began a war that was to engulf much of the world, and in 1917 we, too, were caught up in it.

After fifty years of peace our boys were sent off to war. Boys from city streets, hillbillies who had never been away from their southern mountains, college boys, farm boys, were sent to a far-away continent to fight. Seventeen-year-olds, too young to enlist, rushed over to join the Lafayette Flying Corps and flew funny little crates, as if it were a game to go up before breakfast and shoot down enemy planes.

They were sent off with slogans and songs, because this was a war "to make the world safe for democracy," and "the war to end war." It did not do what was hoped for, but it did bring us closer to the rest of the world and its problems forever.

P.F.

Another book for Clara.

"The only sin is to live in outworn patterns."

Contents

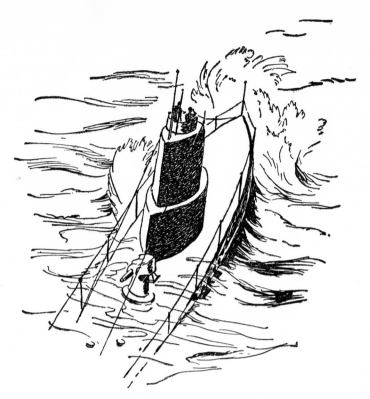

Queenstown Patrol

BY EDWARD ELLSBERG

"Your last chance, Mr. Parker!"

Commander Wilson fairly snapped out his words.

"One more breakdown on the L-18, and back you go to Annapolis, instructing midshipmen; that is, if they'll have you there. Otherwise you'll go to Guam till this war's over!"

Lieutenant Parker nervously twisted the visor of his cap, with red face and clenched teeth listened silently to the stinging reprimand.

The irate commander caught his breath, added, "Two boats in this flotilla are already wearing chevrons for sinking U-boats, while all you've done is to break down on three patrols and get towed in!" He glowered up at the L-18's skipper, paused again.

Parker waited a moment for Commander Wilson to continue, then looking into the stern face before him, hesitantly began to explain. He was curtly interrupted.

"Wartime, Mr. Parker. No excuses!" The flotilla commander turned abruptly in his chair, started to examine the chart spread on the table before him. The interview was over.

The dazed lieutenant paused in the midst of his explanation, stared at the broad back before him; then his jaws clicked firmly to. "Aye, aye, sir!" He turned on his heel, stumbled out of the cabin.

His last chance! Parker looked across the deck of the mother ship, his eyes sweeping for an instant the hills that circled the Irish Queenstown harbor, then gazed down hopelessly at the L-18 moored alongside the tender. What ailed that damn pig, anyway? It was not his fault, nor his crew's either, if the mass of junk that had been squeezed into that sleek hull below there was continually breaking down.

Parker stepped to the port rail, looked overboard. A tangle of lines led from a cargo port in the high side of the *Melville*, disappeared down an open hatch just forward of the L-18's conning tower. Through those lines the submarine was sucking compressed air, distilled water, electricity for her batteries; storing up the vital energy necessary for her next patrol. Outboard of the L-18 were three sister submarines, and on the *Melville's* starboard side were two more—her litter of pigs, sucking greedily away at the mother ship's lines.

Parker ducked through the rail, seized the top rung of the Jacob's ladder, scrambled down, the rope ladder swaying violently against the steel plates of the *Melville* as he descended.

Dungarees smeared with grease, white cap oil-soaked and hardly recognizable as ever having been the starched and gold-laced headgear of a once smart naval officer, face grimy with dirt and perspiration, Lieutenant Parker painfully dragged his strained body off the top of the starboard diesel engine, where, jammed between the sloping inner hull of the submarine and the cylinder heads, he had been struggling to adjust the fuel-oil sprays.

Abaft him, in the passage, a weary gang of machinist's mates surveyed the maze of cams and valves on the engines, turned tired eyes on their skipper as he slid off the cylinder and landed on the floor plates alongside them.

"Well, Mac, they look O.K. to me." Parker, his neck still aching from his cramped position over the diesels, faced his chief machinist's mate, nodded stiffly.

"They oughta be, Captain," replied McCarthy. "Since the *Walton* towed us in the night before last, there ain't a man in this gang's had an hour's sleep. We been working on them engines steady, and whatever else breaks down on the next patrol, it ain't gonna be them diesels."

"It had better not be *anything* else, either," said Parker ruefully. "The old man just got through chewing me out on the *Melville*. Said we were a disgrace to the Navy—broken down at sea now on three patrols straight—and if it happened again, he'd put someone aboard that knew how to operate a pigboat. What ails this tub, anyway? The other pigs have managed to keep on moving."

"The way she's built, I guess," answered McCarthy. "She's a war baby. Some shipyard made a record on her, built her complete in four months from duct keel to conning tower, sorta stunt to show how they were doing their bit to win the war. And this is the result. Nothing's right. When it's not one thing busting down, it's two. I wish I was back on a battlewagon, or one of them boats they built in peacetime when they had time to do a job. This bucket's gonna be our finish sure."

"Not if I know it," snapped out the skipper. "You carried out your orders, Mac?"

"Yeh, I done what you said. There ain't a piece of machinery inside this hull that us engineers ain't gone over to make sure she's right. Up forward, Wilson and the torpedo gang have done the same for their gear, and Sparks here has gone over the electric outfit from stem to stern. Nothing in the boat that we could get hands on ain't been overhauled; only the rudders and the gear outside is left. If you want that inspected you'll have to put the boat in dry dock. And lemme tell you, Captain, the crew's all shot. They ain't had no rest for forty-eight hours; the first thing you know, they'll be going to sleep standing up."

"No, Mac, we can't dry-dock her. Orders are to sail at dusk. Turn all hands in except the watch; let them get what rest they can till we get out. There'll be mighty little rest for them once we're out playing hide-and-seek with Fritzie!"

A vague mass loomed in the darkness off the starboard side. Lieutenant Parker glanced up hastily at it. Daunt Rock. They were passing through the rocky cleft that formed the entrance to Queenstown harbor.

"Right a little!"

"Right a little, sir!" echoed the quartermaster, swinging the steering control over for a moment.

"Steady now. Follow the lights."

"Aye, aye, sir!"

Ahead in the darkness, two faint points, perhaps a hundred yards apart, gleamed fitfully, bobbing up and down against the black background of the night—the hooded stern lights of the two mine sweepers clearing a safe passage to the open sea for the L-18. Between those boats a wire cable sawed through the depths, sweeping for mines sowed by enemy submarines outside the harbor.

Anxiously Parker watched the steering, keeping always in the wake of that sweep. At half speed the L-18 plowed through the night, a safe mile astern of her shepherding convoy.

The submarine started to pitch sluggishly as she met the ocean waves; spray broke over the chariot bridge, drenched the quartermaster, soaked the officer crouching behind him in the confined space between the binnacle and the periscope shears; a trickle of water ran down the open hatch at their feet, gathered in a little pool in the control room below. Parker pulled the helmet of his windbreaker lower over his forehead, wiped the salt spray from his eyes, peered steadily ahead over the binnacle, conning the ship to keep it squarely between those protecting lights.

A thud, a distant roar, a cloud of white foam shone for an instant against the black water ahead. The light on their port bow danced violently a few seconds. The L-18 shook uneasily a moment, then settled down again to the steady pounding of her diesels.

"Another egg," muttered Parker. "Funny how the Heinies always know when a ship's coming out!"

"Easy enough, skipper," growled the quartermaster, his eyes glued on the patch of froth ahead where the mine had exploded. "Queenstown's full of spies. Lucky for us we had them sweeps. That egg was right in our path!"

Parker nodded. Lucky, yes. For the L-18 was steaming squarely through a roiled mass of foam, standing out sharply in the dark ocean. He glanced ahead. There were the twin lights, a hundred yards apart, moving steadily on through the night as if nothing had happened. He owed his luck to the mine sweepers, unromantic trawlers manned by fishermen, steaming unconcernedly through the mine fields clearing a path for the fighting ships. Parker shook his head. A tough life on those sweeps. Fine chance of striking mines themselves. Of course, their light draft allowed them to steam right over a mine without contacting it. That is, if Heinie had his mines all set at the right depths. But occasionally he didn't, and one floated too close to the surface for even a light-draft trawler to pass over. A tough life on those mine sweeps. He shook his head again. Not for him.

"We're clear, Captain. The sweeps is heading back!" mumbled the helmsman.

Parker turned, looked over the edge of the chariot bridge. The lights had veered to port, stopped while they heaved in their kites and reeled in the sweep wire. A sharp flicker of light pierced the darkness. A blinker tube was flashing at them from the wheelhouse of the nearest vessel. In dots and dashes came the message: "Good luck."

The flickering ceased, the dim guide lights on the trawlers were suddenly turned off, the L-18 pounded ahead through the darkness into the open sea. They were clear, in water so deep the Germans could not anchor mines. A brief command, the L-18 turned to starboard, headed for the seas to the west of Ireland where the troopships of America, jammed full of doughboys, were rushing reinforcements to the hard-pressed western front.

"Good luck!" Parker repeated the message gloomily, strained his eyes ahead where the low bow of his submarine plunged into the sea. Good luck! The L-18 had meant anything but that to him so far. Would she hang together this cruise? His last chance. Disconsolately he wondered what a tour on Guam was like. A mere speck in the Pacific, no place for an officer in wartime. He gripped the rail, stared ahead into the night. No tour on Guam for him!

"Silence in the boat!"

At diving stations, the crew of the L-18 leaned tensely over their controls. The pounding of the diesels ceased suddenly. A strange quiet gripped the hull, broken only by the sharp hiss of air whistling out of the vents as the L-18 went awash.

In the center of the control room, McCarthy heaved around on a huge valve wheel, screwing home the main air inlet to the diesels. A bang. The quartermaster above slammed closed the conning-tower hatch, slid down the ladder into the control room, gripped the steering lever.

With his eyes glued to the depth gauge on the port bulkhead, Parker watched as the needle registered their sinking.

McCarthy gave his valve a final twist, reported, "Outboard ventilation valve secured, sir!"

Parker nodded. Twenty feet, the deck was just going under.

"Ready on the main motors, sir!"

"One third ahead!" Without taking his eyes from the gauge, the skipper stepped to the periscope, watched their rapidly increasing depth.

The hiss of air ceased; a tiny jet of water shot out the telltale from the ballast vent line. A seaman hastily closed the cock, called out, "Ballast tanks flooded, sir."

"Aye, aye. Close all the vents!"

More valves were hurriedly screwed down, reported closed. The L-18 kept sinking. Forty feet on the gauge.

"Enough!" called Parker sharply. "Hold her at forty! Standard speed, both motors!"

Diving wheels twirled, down went the controllers, the whir of electric motors filled the boat. Parker pressed a button. A slight grinding broke out as the periscope tube rose slowly from the well at his feet, came to full elevation, stopped. He pressed his face against the rubber eyepiece, looked out.

A few faint streaks of red glowed in the east, lighted dimly the dark circle of sky and sea visible through the periscope. The day was breaking. He swung his lens around, swept the horizon. Nothing in sight.

For the hundredth time Parker looked at the crumpled radio message on the chart board. He knew it by heart now.

> From: C in C, Queenstown.
> To: USS L-18.
> U-6 reported operating in your square. Stop. Use utmost endeavors to make contact.

Parker smiled ruefully. Only too well he realized the U-6 was there. Would he ever forget those drifting corpses he had glimpsed yesterday, the sightless eyes staring down his periscope, the gray sea dotted with the bloated bodies of men and horses through which he had picked his way gingerly as the L-18 swam slowly through the wreckage where the torpedoed *Morentic* had gone down? Yes, the U-6 was in his square.

And if it had not been for that destroyer, he might have made the contact the C in C was so anxious about. He groaned at the recollection. Infernal luck! Midnight, the L-18 was cruising slowly awash, her engines barely turning over, all hands on the bridge straining their ears for the noise of pounding diesels. Their enemy, they knew, must be on the surface somewhere, running engines full power, recharging batteries for his next day's work. The L-18 had caught her radio code signals, reporting no doubt to far-off Germany her success in sinking the horse transport; had heard her chattering the gossip of the war zone with sister U-boats scattered over the seas off Ireland. Strong signals—she was close to them. Cautiously Parker had zigzagged back and forth, seeking the bearing on which his antennae caught the signals loudest, then headed carefully in on that bearing. He remembered the sudden thrill when a familiar throb came to them faintly across the heaving seas, when through his night glasses he had picked up the vague outline of a distant conning tower silhouetted against the dark horizon.

And he had made a perfect approach. With engines stopped to prevent any noise which might alarm the enemy, he had stealthily crept in on his motors to within a mile, submerged to periscope depth to avoid any chance of being seen, and full speed had moved in to make his attack on his unsuspecting prey, torpedoes ready, his finger on the firing button, his target broadside on, success assured.

C'est la guerre! He bit his lip at the recollection. His radioman, white-faced, had stumbled out of the little soundproof booth abaft him with startling news. A destroyer! The high pitched note of her propellers was ringing in his microphones!

And almost before the breathless operator had blurted out his message, Parker, his eye still pressed to the periscope, saw a streak of fire flash through the darkness, a brilliant glare as the tracer shell burst, and in that flash of light the U-6 brilliantly outlined with men madly scrambling down her conning tower, while she moved slowly ahead, started to settle in a crash dive. Then darkness again.

In anguish, Parker had taken a wild chance

pressed the trigger, fired a torpedo at his vanishing prey. He had missed. Range too long, aim bad, poor run on his torpedo? He never knew. The U-6 had disappeared before he could fire again. In the rush of events that followed, only the L-18 had occupied his thoughts.

"Hard dive!"

With diving planes at full depression, they had plunged suddenly from periscope depth to eighty feet. And just in time.

A sharp explosion. The L-18 shook violently; her white-faced crew clung to their controls to save themselves. A depth bomb. Was it meant for them or the U-6? Who knew? To a destroyer every submarine was an enemy. Shoot first, investigate afterward.

A little sick, Parker had hesitated a moment. Should he come up? A salvo of four-inch shells might come crashing into his hull before he could get the lid open and his Very recognition signals bursting in the air.

Another crash, and then at brief intervals a series of them. The L-18 quivered with each shock. The destroyer was laying a pattern of depth bombs as she whirled in a figure eight over the spot where the U-6 had disappeared. Soon she would stop, listen for propellers. And if she picked them up instead of the U-6 a shower of depth bombs would come raining down on them. Parker's indecision vanished.

"Stop the motors!"

Without headway to overcome her negative buoyancy, the L-18 commenced sinking. One hundred feet, two hundred feet, two hundred and fifty feet. In agony Parker had watched the gauge. Bottom at fifty fathoms according to the chart. Two hundred feet was their working depth, three hundred feet their safe limit. Was the chart accu- ? Three hundred feet, still sinking. Petrified, the men gripped their controls, watched the gauge. And then, at three hundred and five feet, a gentle bump, the L-18 came softly to rest in the mud. A sigh of relief echoed audibly through the control room; tense limbs relaxed; his crew breathed once more.

The shocks of the depth bombs were fainter now, ceased shortly. Crouched alongside the operator in the tiny radio booth, receivers jammed over his ears, Parker listened on the microphones to the shrill note of the propellers on the surface, singing in his ears one moment as the destroyer darted ahead, then ceasing abruptly as she stopped her engines to listen. Back and forth, it seemed endlessly, that note rang through the sea as the destroyer searched the depths, then faded gradually as the baffled ship swung in ever-widening circles, trying to pick up the trail of her submerged enemy.

But in vain. Somewhere in the depths, nestling quietly in the mud like himself, Parker visioned the U-6, shuddered at the thought. The vessel which a few minutes before he had been ready to blow out of the water, was now, like the L-18, a hunted fugitive, her crew crouching in terror like his own in their cramped compartments, shaking at the fear that something might float up, give their hiding place away, send a hurtling bomb, set to burst at the bottom, down on the hull to crush their fragile shell, bury them forever in the mud and the ooze of the ocean floor.

But it had not happened. The destroyer had vanished, seeking a submarine still under way. After two hours on the bottom, Parker had partly blown his safety tank, floated up to thirty feet, pushed up his periscope, made a careful search to insure that neither friend nor foe was in sight on the surface, then hastily blown the rest of the safety tank to get his conning tower fully out of water.

With the lid open to get air for the engines, he had hurried full speed through the night to put at least five miles between himself and the scene of the battle, lest the U-6 should bob up and catch him unawares. Then, with propellers disconnected and engines working full power, the L-18 spent the rest of the dark hours recharging storage cells, while her thankful crew took turns, four at a time, in clambering up on the little bridge, hardly six feet out of water, and breathing in the free air of heaven.

Once more Lieutenant Parker swept the horizon with his periscope, scanned the waves as the dawn broke over the sea. Nothing in sight on the surface—the destroyer had vanished.

At dead-slow speed, the L-18 swam through the sea, using only enough of her precious electricity to give her diving planes control and hold the depth against the slight positive buoyancy which Parker was carrying on the boat for safety's sake. Slowly the minutes dragged on, grew to hours. The sun rose high in the heavens, no longer threw a blinding glare into the periscope eye as it swung around. The submarine wheeled gradually in a high spiral, the search curve on which Parker hoped to find his enemy.

Inside the boat, the air grew thicker; the odor of oil, of acid fumes from the batteries, permeated the control room; the atmosphere became laden with carbon dioxide from being breathed over and over again. Parker noted that the air of alertness with which his men had taken the boat under, was gradually vanishing; heads drooped over the controls, lackluster eyes gazed vacantly at gauges, pored uncomprehendingly over the switchboard. His own head started to ache; his eyes, strained by the high-powered lenses in the periscope, burned in their sockets; his head felt heavy, his mind thick. Six hours under; eight more to go before darkness settled again and they could safely come up. He wondered vaguely what had become of the U-6. She must be taking it easier. Unaware of the presence of another submarine, she would spend part of her time, at least, awash with her lid open, taking a fresh supply of air every hour or so, perhaps even running on her diesels to conserve her batteries, safe in the thought that she could spot a surface ship and dive long before such a small object as her conning tower could be seen by any approaching vessel. Parker thanked his luck for that unawareness; at least he had not given himself away by coming up and firing recognition signals while the U-6 was still around. Unquestionably the Germans had dived the night before without the slightest knowledge that the sudden rush of that hurtling destroyer was all that had saved them from certain disaster.

Well, it was nearly over. With the night, his patrol was finished; the L-18 would move hastily out of that square, get well clear before the L-7, relieving them, came on the patrol in the morning. A grim situation, all right. Once his relief arrived, if he was still there submerged, she would certainly blow him out of the water if she sighted his periscope; if he ran on the surface and disclosed his identity as an Allied man-of-war, then a torpedo from the lurking U-6 was almost certain to do the same. A rotten life in the pigs—fair game for everybody, submerged or afloat, with that blasted air to eat your lungs out while under water, and the deafening roar of diesels to ruin your sleep and drive you crazy while you charged at night; and always in the background of your mind, while running submerged, that gnawing fear of the sea, lying in wait to crush your boat and flatten you out if your pig went out of control for a brief instant and sank just a few feet too deep before you caught her.

Parker shook his head, tried to throw off the weight

that seemed to press in on his throbbing temples. He was lucky—his last day on patrol. Tonight when they broke surface, and the engines started to pound again, it would be to drive them home to Queenstown, not to charge batteries for another day of torture in the depths.

And nothing had broken down. He could face Commander Wilson on the *Melville;* his men instead of overhauling engines, could spend their time in part on liberty. Cork, even Queenstown, after a week jammed inside this pig, would be heaven for a sailor. No breakdowns. Perhaps the jinx was shaken at last. With an effort, the dopey skipper pulled his thoughts back from the rest that awaited him in Queenstown, pressed his eye against the lens in front of him.

A vista of gray waves met his sight, undulating gently, capped with patches of white foam here and there, merging in the distant haze with a cloudy sky. Slowly he revolved the periscope tube, scanned the horizon, searched the intervening sea. Nothing in sight—no ships, no smoke, only the vast sweep of the deserted ocean. Perfunctorily he finished his inspection, pressed the motor button, started to house the periscope.

A glint of sunshine flashed into his eye. Queer. The sun was too high for that. He stopped housing, squinted out the lens. His heart skipped a beat.

There, half a mile off on the starboard bow, its tapering length glistening in the sun, was a periscope!

Parker leaned forward, punched a voice-tube button, shouted excitedly, "Torpedo room! Stand by. U-boat on the starboard bow!"

As if jolted by an electric current, the drooping figures around the control room stiffened suddenly, looked toward their skipper. Forgotten were the bad air, the cramped quarters. Tense figures gripped the controls again; eager eyes scanned their instruments, ready for action. The enemy was in sight!

His temples throbbing wildly, Parker pressed his face again to the eyepiece, looked hurriedly at the bearing. Forty degrees on his starboard bow. They must bring her dead ahead.

"Ten degrees right rudder!" His voice sounded strange, far-off, as, eye glued to the periscope, the words hissed out.

"Ten right, sir," echoed the helmsman just forward of him.

The L-18 started to swing. Parker dared not even for an instant take his gaze off that thin steel finger dancing in the far-off waves; if he lost it in the whitecaps, he might never pick up that gleam again. Slowly he walked his periscope round as the submarine answered her rudder and the bearing of his target drew ahead. The L-18 heeled gently in her turn. Parker clung tightly to the handles to maintain his balance. Only ten degrees on the bow now.

"Meet her!"

Hurriedly Lieutenant Parker tried to estimate the course of that periscope. Was the U-6 bows-on to him or was she broadside? Only in the latter case would a slim submarine offer target enough for a decent shot. Tensely he watched the wisps of spray play round the distant tube, caught a tiny wake on its far side, switched in the high-magnification lens to study it. The field of view in his periscope narrowed; the distant waves seemed suddenly to leap closer; he was startled to see that the eye of the enemy periscope was pointing directly at him, that the two submarines were headed for each other!

For an instant, his blood froze, his jaw dropped, he stared open-mouthed, hypnotized by that tiny lens gleaming at him across half a mile of tossing seas.

"Steady on the course now." The quartermaster's voice broke the silence of the control room.

With a jerk, Parker came back to life. No more maneuvering, he must get his torpedo in first!

He fumbled for the firing pistol, stared out the lens. The enemy periscope was dead ahead; his boat had steadied. Parker's fingers gripped the firing handle, started to squeeze the trigger. A vague recollection; he paused. The torpedo room had not reported ready.

For the first time since sighting the enemy, Parker tore his eye from the rubber shield, stooped hastily, and looked forward through the open watertight doors into the torpedo room, where, outboard of the shining bronze covers of the tubes, he glimpsed the broad back of his chief torpedo man straining frenziedly over a wheel.

Parker straightened up, punched a button, sang out into the voice tube, "Torpedo room there! What's wrong?"

The reply fell like a bludgeon on his ear.

"The bow cap's jammed, Captain! We can't rotate it to uncover any of the torpedo tubes outside."

Parker's heart sank like lead. The bow cap—the spherical outside fairwater over his nest of torpedoes, with a solitary opening which had to register with the mouth of the tube to be fired before the missile could be ejected—jammed! And with none of his four tubes in line with the opening.

Parker stooped, stared forward into the torpedo room where his men were struggling with the rotating gear. A brawny seaman seized a spoke, added his weight to the chief's on the wheel.

Broken down again! In a daze, the stunned skipper watched the straining torpedo men while the full meaning of the accident sank into his brain. The glistening bodies of his torpedoes, the grim warheads full of TNT that a moment before, so he thought, had needed but the pressure of his finger to spring from his tubes toward the U-6—imprisoned now behind that fatal cap, impossible of release! The L-18 had suddenly become impotent, unable to attack, helpless even to defend herself. The shock of that destroyer's depth bombs last night must have sprung the shafting, jammed the operating gears.

As he watched, a third seaman sprang forward with a huge monkey wrench, slipped its jaws over the rim of the wheel for a lever, flung his body hard down on the handle. No use. The wheel refused to turn; the bow cap was frozen tight with all the tubes sealed off.

Stunned by the situation, Parker turned to find terrified faces staring at him from all sides; the afterend of the room was filled with engineers. Like a flash the news of their disaster had spread through the boat; unconsciously the men were starting to edge toward the escape hatch beneath the conning tower.

Escape! A cracked laugh died in his throat. Why worry over the hatches? The U-6 was close aboard. Another few seconds and the quickest way out would be through their smashed side.

"Hard dive!"

The order burst from his parched lips, echoed like a bomb through the room. Diving wheels spun madly, controllers went over to "Full speed ahead." The L-18 started to seek safety in the depths. Ignoring his crew, Parker flung himself at the periscope, got a fleeting glimpse of that deadly eye staring at him not two hundred yards away, saw a fine cloud of spray spout through the surface, a streak of bubbles form in the waves, race for him. Then the sea washed over his periscope, suddenly blotted out everything.

"They've fired!" groaned Parker. He twisted his head from the useless lens, looked feverishly over his shoulder at

the depth gauge. Still forty feet, the needle hardly starting to move. Would they never get down? Blanched faces,
wild eyes all around followed his glance; trembling lips
muttered curses watching that dial.

A few seconds now, the torpedo would strike. Parker
looked despairingly toward his torpedo room, at the men
still struggling there. "One more breakdown and back you
go to. . . ." Commander Wilson's threat flashed through
his mind. "Annapolis." One more breakdown. How deep
was the ooze on the ocean bottom? "Or Guam till this
war's over." Wilson was wrong. A shattered submarine buried in the mud. Forty-five feet on that gauge now. No hope.
How many seconds since the U-6 had fired? Only ten seconds needed by a torpedo to cover that distance. His gaze
wandered over the side of the submarine, covered everywhere with intricate machinery. Where would their hull
suddenly burst open, let the ocean come pouring through?
One more breakdown. He cursed the builders of this pigboat.

A deafening crash, the L-18 heeled drunkenly to port,
the bow shot up at a sharp angle. The end. Curses, prayers,
a tangle of arms and legs, a knot of crazed seamen struggling for the ladder to the conning tower; then a sudden
silence as the fighting men stopped, looked wonderingly
around for the rushing water that should be flooding the
boat.

Parker, in a daze, extricated himself from the Kingston
levers in the port bilges, groped his way uncertainly back
to his station. The water! Where was it? Which compartment had that torpedo torn apart?

Incredulously he shot a glance through the forward
bulkhead, then aft through the quivering hull. The deck
was badly heeled; mattresses, men, tools, charts, were

sprawled out everywhere; but there was no cataract of water rushing toward him—yet.

What had happened? That explosion, the shock that had tossed them through the seas like a bubble? The torpedo had hit somewhere; in a damaged boat Parker dared not stay submerged.

"Blow all ballast! Hard rise!"

His sharp command rang through the control room. Bewildered men, startled to find themselves still alive, untangled themselves from the manifolds, scrambled out of the bilges, staggered back to their controls. The shrill whistle of compressed air, the grinding of gears, the whir of motors echoed through the boat as the men of the L-18 fought to check their descent, to rise to the surface, escape from their prison. Ballast water poured overboard, propellers drove viciously ahead, diving planes at full elevation shot the trembling shell upward.

An instant, then their conning tower burst clear, the submarine rocked unsteadily in the seaway. Parker scrambled up the ladder into the conning tower, tripped the lever. The hatch flew back, he crawled through. Water was still pouring off the chariot bridge; his low deck was just breaking from the sea. Swiftly his eye ran along the hull from the jagged net cutter in the bow to the tapering stern. Unbelievingly his glance swept back. No damage anywhere.

And yet, that explosion. The torpedo had certainly struck something. What?

Half a ship length ahead, a spreading patch of oil caught his eye. He stared, thunderstruck. That was where the U-6 had been!

Something rubbed his legs. He looked down. McCarthy was squeezing through the hatch. Below him, Parker caught a glimpse of the conning tower jammed with men, struggling to get out. In a trice, his chief machinist's mate was alongside him; seamen were pouring out the hatch, crowding the chariot bridge, clambering down the outside of the conning tower to the half-awash deck below.

A huge bubble of air rose through the sea into the middle of the slick, frothed a moment, then subsided as the oily ring widened out, a patch of water strangely smooth in an ocean of tossing waves and spray-tipped crests. Anxiously Parker scanned the sea—no periscope anywhere. But there in the bubbles and the froth, a few bits of oil-soaked wreckage were breaking surface, shattered fragments of a submarine's deck!

"Look, skipper, this pile of junk rates a chevron on her conning tower from now on. We're heroes! The L-18's sunk a U-boat!" McCarthy pointed excitedly at the bits of wood and huge globules of oil gushing upward near their bow.

Lieutenant Parker nodded slowly. "Guess you're right, Mac, she's gone. But what under the sun's happened? I saw that torpedo start for us."

"The gyro in the tail of that torpedo must have stuck with the rudder hard over, and made it run in a circle so it curved round and soaked the U-6 instead of us. I seen that happen once in target practice, but never with a war shot." He mopped the beads of sweat off his forehead. "I guess pigboats and tin fish ain't no more reliable in the Heinie navy than they are in your Uncle Sam's."

Parker looked forward to his bow, in full surface trim now, vaguely made out just below the water line the rounded outlines of the torpedo-tube cap, watched a moment his torpedo gang clustered on the forecastle, futilely staring down at the iron hemisphere.

He shook his head, gripped the engine telegraph, turned a strained face toward McCarthy. "Well, Mac, we'd better get under way for home now while we're still live heroes. Our patrol's about over, and we're helpless anyway with that bow cap jammed."

"Aye, aye, sir," said McCarthy with a grin. "Let's make knots for Queenstown before this pig breaks down, or Commander Wilson will be after us!"

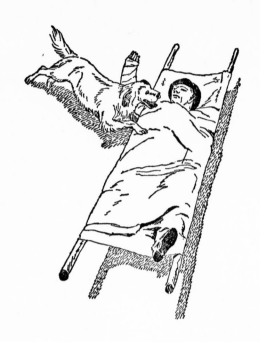

Verdun Belle

BY ALEXANDER WOOLLCOTT

I first heard the saga of Verdun Belle's adventure as it
was being told one June afternoon under a drowsy apple
tree in the troubled valley of the Marne.

The story began in a chill, grimy Lorraine village, where,
in hovels and haymows, a disconsolate detachment of
United States marines lay waiting for the order to go up
into that maze of trenches of which the crumbling traces
still weave a haunted web around the citadel bearing the
immortal name of Verdun.

Into this village at dusk one day in the early spring of
1918 there came out of space a shabby, lonesome dog—a
squat setter of indiscreet, complex, and unguessable an-
cestry.

One watching her as she trotted intently along the aromatic village street would have sworn that she had an important engagement with the mayor and was, regretfully, a little late.

At the end of the street she came to where a young buck private lounged glumly on a doorstep. Halting in her tracks, she sat down to contemplate him. Then, satisfied seemingly by what she sensed and saw, she came over and flopped down beside him in a most companionable manner, settling herself comfortably as if she had come at last to her long journey's end. His pleased hand reached over and played with one silken chocolate-colored ear.

Somehow that gesture sealed a compact between those two. There was thereafter no doubt in either's mind that they belonged to each other for better or for worse, in sickness and in health, through weal and woe, world without end.

She ate when and what he ate. She slept beside him in the hay, her muzzle resting on his leg so that he could not get up in the night and go forgetfully back to America without her noticing it.

To the uninitiated onlookers her enthusiasm may not have been immediately explicable. In the eyes of his top sergeant and his company clerk he may well have seemed an undistinguished warrior, freckle-faced and immensely indifferent to the business of making the world safe for democracy.

Verdun Belle thought him the most charming person in all the world. There was a loose popular notion that she had joined up with the company as mascot and belonged to them all. She affably let them think so, but she had her own ideas on the subject.

When they moved up into the line she went along and was so obviously trench-broken that they guessed she had already served a hitch with some French regiment in that once desperate region. They even built up the not implausible theory that she had come to them lonely from the grave of some little soldier in faded horizon blue.

Certainly she knew trench ways, knew in the narrowest of passages how to keep out from underfoot, and was so well aware of the dangers of the parapet that a plate of chicken bones up there would not have interested her. She even knew what gas was, and after a reminding whiff of it became more than reconciled to the regulation gas mask, which they patiently wrecked for all subsequent human use because an unimaginative War Department had not foreseen the peculiar anatomical specifications of Verdun Belle.

In May, when the outfit was engaged in the exhausting activities which the High Command was pleased to describe as "resting," Belle thought it a convenient time to present an interested but amply forewarned regiment with seven wriggling casuals, some black and white and mottled as a mackerel sky, some splotched with the same brown as her own.

These newcomers complicated the domestic economy of the leathernecks' haymow, but they did not become an acute problem until that memorable night late in the month when breathless word bade these troops be up and away.

The Second Division of the A.E.F. was always being thus picked up by the scruff of the neck and flung across France. This time the enemy had snapped up Soissons and Rheims and were pushing with dreadful ease and speed toward the remembering Marne.

Foch had called upon the Americans to help stem the tide. Ahead of the marines, as they scrambled across the monotonous plain of the Champagne, there lay amid the ripening wheat fields a mean and hilly patch of timber called Belleau Wood. Verdun Belle went along.

The leatherneck had solved the problem of the puppies by drowning four and placing the other three in a basket he had begged from a village woman.

His notion that he could carry the basket would have come as a shock to whatever functionary back in Washington designed the marine pack, which, with its neat assortment of food supplies, extra clothing, emergency restoratives, and gruesome implements for destruction, had been so painstakingly calculated to exhaust the capacity of the human back. But in his need the young marine somehow contrived to add an item not in the regulations, namely, one basket containg three unweaned and faintly resentful puppies.

By night and by day the troop movement was made, now in little wheezing trains, now in swarming lorries, now afoot.

Sometimes Belle's crony rode. Sometimes (under pressure of popular clamor against the room he was taking up) he would yield up his place to the basket and jog along with his hand on the tailboard, with Belle trotting behind him.

All the soldiers in Christendom seemed to be moving across France to some nameless crossroads over the hill. Obviously this was no mere shift from one quiet sector to another. They were going to war.

Everyone had assured the stubborn youngster that he would not be able to manage, and now misgivings settled on him like crows.

He guessed that Verdun Belle must be wondering too. He turned to assure her that everything would be all right. She was not there. Ahead of him, behind him, there was no sign of her. No one within call had seen her quit the line.

He kept telling himself she would show up. But the day went and the night came without her.

He jettisoned the basket and pouched the pups in his forest-green shirt in the manner of kangaroos. In the morning one of the three was dead. And the problem of transporting the other two was now tangled by the circumstance that he had to feed them.

An immensely interested old woman in the village where they halted at sunup, vastly amused by this spectacle of a soldier trying to carry two nursing puppies to war, volunteered some milk for the cup of his mess kit, and with much jeering advice from all sides, and, by dint of the eye dropper from his pack, he tried sheepishly to be a mother to the two waifs. The attempt was not shiningly successful.

He itched to pitch them over the fence. But if Verdun Belle had not been run over by some thundering camion, if she lived she would find him, and then what would he say when her eyes asked what he had done with the pups?

So, as the order was shouted to fall in, he hitched his pack to his back and stuffed his charges back into his shirt.

Now, in the morning light, the highway was choked. Down from the lines in agonized, grotesque rout came the stream of French life from the threatened countryside, jumbled fragments of fleeing French regiments. But America was coming up the road.

It was a week in which the world held its breath.

The battle was close at hand now. Field hospitals, jostling in the river of traffic, sought space to pitch their tents. The top sergeant of one such outfit was riding on the driver's seat of an ambulance. Marines in endless number were moving up fast.

It was one of these who, in a moment's halt, fell out of

line, leaped to the step of the blockaded ambulance, and looked eagerly into the medico top sergeant's eyes.

"Say, buddy," whispered the youngster, "take care of these for me. I lost their mother in the jam."

The top found his hands closing on two drowsy pups.

All that day the field-hospital personnel was harried by the task of providing nourishment for the two casuals who had been thus unexpectedly attached to them for rations. Once established in a farmhouse (from which they were promptly shelled out), the top went over the possible provender and found that the pups were not yet equal to a diet of bread, corn syrup, and corned willy. A stray cow, loosed from her moorings in the great flight, was browsing tentatively in the next field, and two orderlies who had carelessly reminisced of life on their farms back home were detailed to induce her co-operation.

But the bombardment had brought out a certain moody goatishness in this cow, and she would not let them come near her. After a hot and maddening chase that lasted two hours, the two milkmen reported a complete failure to their disgusted chief.

The problem was still unsolved at sundown, and the pups lay faint in their bed of absorbent cotton out in the garden, when, bringing up the rear of a detachment of marines that straggled past, there trotted a brown-and-white setter.

"It would be swell if she had milk in her," the top sergeant said reflectively, wondering how he could salvage the mascot of an outfit on the march.

But his larcenous thoughts were waste. At the gate she halted dead in her tracks, flung her head high to sniff the air, wheeled sharp to the left and became just a streak of brown and white against the ground. The entire staff came out and formed a jostling circle to watch the family reunion.

After that it was tacitly assumed that these casuals belonged. When the hospital was ordered to shift further back beyond the reach of the whining shells, Verdun Belle and the pups were intrusted to an ambulance driver and went along in style. They all moved—bag, baggage, and livestock—into the deserted little Château of the Guardian Angel, of which the front windows were curtained against the eyes and dust of the road, but of which the rear windows looked out across drooping fruit trees upon a sleepy, murmurous, multicolored valley, fair as the Garden of the Lord.

The operating tables, with acetylene torches to light them, were set up in what had been a tool shed. Cots were strewn in the orchard alongside. Thereafter for a month there was never rest in that hospital.

The surgeons and orderlies spelled each other at times, snatching morsels of sleep and returning a few hours later to relieve the others. But Verdun Belle took no time off. Between cat naps in the corner, due attentions to her restive brood, and an occasional snack for herself, she managed somehow to be on hand for every ambulance, cursorily examining each casualty as he was lifted to the ground.

Then, in the four o'clock dark of one morning, the orderly bending over a stretcher that had just been rested on the ground was hit by something that half bowled him over.

The projectile was Verdun Belle. Every quivering inch of her proclaimed to all concerned that here was a case she was personally in charge of. From nose to tail tip she was taut with excitement, and a kind of eager whimpering bubbled up out of her as if she ached to sit back on her haunches and roar to the star-spangled sky but was really too busy at the moment to indulge herself in any release so satisfying to her soul. For here was this mess of a leatherneck of hers to be washed up first. So like him to get all dirty the moment her back was turned! The first thing he knew as he came to was the feel of a rough pink tongue cleaning his ears.

I saw them all next day. An ambling passer-by, I came upon two cots shoved together under an apple tree. Belle and her ravenous pups occupied one of these. On the other the young marine—a gas case, I think, but maybe his stupor was shell shock and perhaps he had merely had a crack on the head—was deep in a dreamless sleep. Before drifting off he had taken the comforting precaution to reach out one hand and close it tight on a silken ear.

Later that day he told me all about his dog. I doubt if I ever knew his name, but some quirk of memory makes me think his home was in West Philadelphia and that he had joined up with the marines when he came out of school.

I went my way before dark and never saw them again, nor ever heard tell what became of the boy and his dog. I never knew when, if ever, he was shipped back into the fight, nor where, if ever, those two met again. It is, you see, a story without an end, though there must be those here and there in this country who witnessed and could set down for us the chapter that has never been written.

I hope there was something prophetic in the closing paragraph of the anonymous account of Verdun Belle which appeared the next week in the A.E.F. newspaper, *The Stars and Stripes*. That paragraph was a benison which ran in this wise:

Before long they would have to ship him on to the evacuation hospital, on from there to the base hospital, on and on and on. It was not very clear to anyone how another separation could be prevented. It was a perplexing question, but they knew in their hearts they could safely leave the answer to someone else. They could leave it to Verdun Belle.

The King of Ypres

BY JOHN BUCHAN

Private Peter Galbraith, of the 3rd Lennox Highlanders, awoke with a splitting headache and the consciousness of an intolerable din. At first he thought it was the whistle from the forge, which a year ago had pulled him from his bed when he was a puddler in Motherwell. He scrambled to his feet, and nearly cracked his skull against a low roof. That, and a sound which suggested that the heavens were made of canvas which a giant hand was rending, cleared his wits and recalled him to the disagreeable present. He lit the dottle in his pipe, and began to piece out his whereabouts.

Late the night before, the remnants of his battalion had been brought in from the Gheluvelt trenches to billets in Ypres, Belgium. That last week he had gone clean off his sleep. He had not been dry for a fortnight, his puttees had rotted away, his greatcoat had disappeared in a mudhole, and he had had no stomach for what food could be got. He had seen half his battalion die before his eyes, and day and night the shells had burst round him till the place looked like the ironworks at Motherwell on a foggy night. The worst of it was that he had never come to grips with the Boches, which he had long decided was the one pleasure left to him in life. He had got far beyond cursing, though he had once had a talent that way. His mind was as sodden as his body, and his thoughts had been focused on the penetrating power of a bayonet when directed against a plump Teutonic chest. There had been a German barber in Motherwell called Schultz, and he imagined the enemy as a million Schultzes—large, round men who talked with the back of their throat.

In billets he had scraped off the worst part of the mud, and drunk half a bottle of wine, which a woman had given him. It tasted like red ink, but anything liquid was better than food. Sleep was what he longed for, but he could not get it. The Boches were shelling the town, and the room he shared with six others seemed as noisy as the Gallowgate on a Saturday night. He wanted to get deep down into the earth where there was no sound; so, while the others snored, he started out to look for a cellar. In the black darkness, while the house rocked to the shell reverberations, he had groped his way down the stairs, found a door which led to another flight, and, slipping and stumbling, had come to a narrow, stuffy chamber which smelled of potatoes. There he had lain down on some sacks and fallen into a frowzy slumber.

His head was spinning, but the hours of sleep had done him good. He felt a slight appetite for breakfast, as well as an intolerable thirst. He groped his way up the stairs, and came out in a dilapidated hall lit by a dim November morning.

There was no sign of the packs which had been stacked there the night before. He looked for a Boche's helmet, which he had brought in as a souvenir, but that was gone. Then he found the room where he had been billeted. It was empty, and only the stale smell of tobacco told of its occupants.

Lonely, disconsolate, and oppressed with thoughts of future punishment, he moved toward the street door. Suddenly the door of a side room opened and a man came out, a furtive figure with a large, pasty face. His pockets bulged and in one hand was a silver candlestick. At the sight of Galbraith he jumped back and held up a pistol.

"Put it down, man, and tell us what's come over this place?" said the soldier. For answer, a bullet sang past his ear and shivered a plaster Venus.

Galbraith gave his enemy the butt of his rifle and laid him out. From his pockets he shook out a mixed collection of loot. He took possession of his pistol, and kicked him with some vehemence into a cupboard.

"That one's a thief," was his spoken reflection. "There's something mighty wrong today."

His head was clearing, and he was getting very wroth. His battalion had gone off and left him in a cellar, and miscreants were abroad. It was time for a respectable man to be up and doing. Besides, he wanted his breakfast. He fixed his bayonet, put the pistol in his pocket, and emerged into the November drizzle.

The streets suddenly were curiously still. The occasional shellfire came to his ears as if through layers of cotton wool. He put this down to dizziness from lack of food, and made his way to what looked like an *estaminet*. The place was full of riotous people who were helping themselves to drinks, while a distracted landlord wrung his hands. He flew to Galbraith, the tears running down his cheeks, and implored him in broken words.

"Where are the English?" he cried. "The *méchants* rob me. Where are the officers?"

"That's what I'm wantin' to know myself," said Galbraith.

"They are gone," wailed the innkeeper. "There is no *gendarme* or anything, and I am rob."

"Where's the police? Get the provost, man. D'ye tell me there's no police left?"

"I am rob," the wail continued. "The *méchants* rob the *magasins* and we will be *assassinés*."

Light was dawning upon Private Galbraith. The British troops had left Ypres for some reason which he could not fathom, and there was no law or order in the little city. At other times he had hated the law as much as any man, and his relations with the police had often been strained. Now he realized that he had done them an injustice. Disorder suddenly seemed to him the one thing intolerable. He was a British soldier—marooned here by no fault of his own— and it was his business to keep up the end of the British Army and impose the king's peace upon the unruly. His temper was getting hot, but he was curiously happy. He marched into the *estaminet*. "Out of here, ye scum!" he bellowed. "*Sortez, ye cochons!*"

The revelers were silent before the apparition. Then one, drunker than the rest, flung a bottle which grazed his right ear. That put the finishing touch to his temper. Roaring like a bull, he was among them, prodding their hinder parts with his bayonet, and now and then reversing his rifle to crack a head. He had not played center forward in the old days at Celtic Park for nothing. The place emptied in a twinkling—all but one man whose legs could not support him. Him Private Galbraith seized by the scruff and the slack of his trousers, and tossed into the street.

"Now I'll have my breakfast," he said to the trembling landlord.

Private Galbraith, much the better for his exercise, made a hearty meal of bread and cold ham, and quenched his thirst with two bottles of Hazebrouck beer. He had also a little brandy, and pocketed the flask, for which the landlord refused all payment. Then, feeling a giant refreshed, he sallied into the street.

"I'm off to look for your provost," he said. "If ye have any more trouble, you'll find me at the town hall."

A shell had plumped into the middle of the causeway, and the place was empty. Private Galbraith, despising shells, swaggered up the open, his disreputable kilt swinging about his putteeless legs, the remnant of a bonnet set well on the side of his shaggy red head, and the light of battle in his eyes. For once he was arrayed on the side of the angels, and the thought encouraged him mightily. The brandy had fired his imagination.

Adventure faced him at the next corner. A woman was struggling with two men—a slim, pale girl with dark hair. No sound came from her lips, but her eyes were bright with terror. Galbraith started to run, shouting sound British oaths. The men let the women go, and turned to face him. One had a pistol, and for the second time that day a bullet just missed its mark. An instant later a clean bayonet thrust had ended the mortal career of the marksman, and the other had taken to his heels.

"I'll learn those lads to be so free with their popguns," said the irate soldier. "Head up, ma'am. It's all done with now. Losh! The woman's fainted!"

Private Galbraith was as shy of women as of his commanding officer, and he had not bargained for this duty. She was clearly a lady from her dress and appearance, and this did not make it easier. He supported her manfully, addressing to her the kind of encouragements which a groom gives to a horse. "Easy now, ma'am. Head up! You've no cause to be feared."

Then he remembered the brandy in his pocket, and with much awkwardness managed to force some drops between her lips. To his vast relief she began to come to. Her eyes opened and stared uncomprehendingly at her preserver. Then she found her voice. "Thank God, the British have come back!" she said in excellent English.

"No, ma'am; not yet. It's just me, Private Galbraith, C Company, 3rd Battalion, Lennox Highlanders. Ye keep some bad lots in this town."

"Alas! What can we do? The place is full of spies, and they will stir up the dregs of the people and make Ypres a hell. Oh, why did the British go? Our good men are all with the army, and there are only old folk and wastrels left."

"Rely upon me, ma'am," said Galbraith stoutly. "I was just setting off to find your provost."

She puzzled at the word, and then understood. "He has gone!" she cried. "The *maire* went to Dunkirk a week ago, and there is no authority in Ypres."

"Then we'll make one. Here's the minister. We'll speak to him."

An old priest, with a lean, grave face, had come up. "Ah, Mam'selle Omèrine," he cried, "the devil in our city is unchained. Who is this soldier?"

The two talked in French, while Galbraith whistled and looked at the sky. A shrapnel shell was bursting behind the cathedral, making a splash of color in the November fog. Then the priest spoke in careful and constrained English.

"There is yet a chance for a strong man. But he must be very strong. Mam'selle will summon her father, Monsieur le Procureur, and we will meet at the *mairie*. I will guide you there, *mon brave*."

The *Grande Place* was deserted, and in the middle there was a new gaping shell hole. At the door of a great building which Galbraith assumed to be the town hall, a feeble old porter was struggling with a man. Galbraith scragged the latter and pitched him into the shell hole. There was a riot going on in a café on the far side, which he itched to have a hand in, but he postponed that pleasure to a more convenient season.

Twenty minutes later, in a noble room with frescoed and tapestried walls, there was a strange conference. The priest was there, and Galbraith, and Mam'selle Omèrine, and her father, Monsieur St. Marais. There was a doctor too, and three elderly citizens, and an old warrior who had left an arm on the Yser. Galbraith took charge, with Mam'-selle as his interpreter, and in half an hour had constituted a Committee of Public Safety. He had nervous folk to deal with.

"The Germans may enter at any moment, and then we will all be hanged," said one.

"No doubt," said Galbraith, "but ye needn't get your throats cut afore they come."

"The city is full of the ill-disposed," said another. "The Boches have their spies in every alley. We who are so few cannot control them."

"If it's spies," said Galbraith firmly, "I'll take on the job by myself. D'ye think a terrier dog's afraid of a few rats?"

In the end he had his way, with Mam'selle's help, and had put some confidence into civic breasts. It took him the best part of the afternoon to collect his posse. He got every wounded Belgian that had the use of his legs, some well-grown boys, one or two ancients, and several dozen robust women. There was no lack of weapons, and he armed the lot with a strange collection of French and English rifles, giving pistols to the section leaders. With the help of the Procureur, he divided the city into beats and gave his followers instructions. They were drastic orders, for the situation craved for violence.

He spent the evening of his life. So far as he remembered afterward, he was in seventeen different scraps. Strayed revelers were leniently dealt with—the canal was a cooling experience. Looters were rounded up, and, if they showed fight, summarily disposed of. One band of bullies made a stout resistance, killed two of his guards, and lost half a dozen dead. He got a black eye, a pistol bullet through his sleeve, a wipe on the cheek from a carving knife, and he lost the remnants of his bonnet. Fifty-two prisoners spent the night in the cellars of the *mairie*.

About midnight he found himself in the tapestried chamber. "We'll have to get a proclamation," he had announced. "A good strong one for we must conduct this job according to the rules." So the Procureur had a document drawn up bidding all inhabitants of Ypres keep indoors except between the hours of ten A.M. and noon, and three and five P.M.; forbidding the sale of alcohol in all forms; and making theft and violence and the carrying of arms punishable by death. There was a host of other provisions which Galbraith imperfectly understood, but when the thing was translated to him he approved its spirit. He signed the document in his large sprawling hand—"Peter Galbraith, 1473, Pvt., 3rd Lennox Highlanders, Acting Provost of Ypres."

"Get that printed," he said, "and put up copies at every street corner and all the public houses. And see that the doors of the publics are boarded up. That'll do for the day. I'm feeling very like my bed."

Mam'selle Omèrine watched him with a smile. She caught his eye and dropped him a curtsy. "Monsieur le Roi d'Ypres," she said.

He blushed hotly.

For the next few days Private Galbraith worked harder than ever before in his existence. For the first time he knew responsibility, and that toil which brings honor with it. He tasted the sweets of office; and he, whose aim in life had been to scrape through with the minimum of exertion, now found himself the inspirer of the maximum in others.

At first he scorned advice, being shy and nervous. Gradually, however, he became glad of other people's wisdom. Especially he leaned on two, Mam'selle Omèrine and her father. Likewise the priest, whom he called the minister.

By the second day the order in Ypres was remarkable. By the third day it was phenomenal; and by the fourth, a tyranny. The little city for the first time in seven hundred years fell under the sway of a despot. A citizen had to be on his best behavior, for the Acting Provost's eye was on him. Never was seen so sober a place. Three permits for alcohol, and no more, were issued, and then only on the plea of medical necessity. Peter handed over to the doctor the flask of brandy he had carried off from the *estaminet*— provosts must set an example.

The Draconian code promulgated the first night was not

adhered to. Looters and violent fellows went to jail instead of the gallows. But three spies were taken and shot after a full trial. That trial was the master effort of Private Galbraith—based on his own regimental experience and memories of a sheriff's court in Lanarkshire, where he had twice appeared for poaching. He was extraordinarily punctilious about forms, and the three criminals—their guilt was clear, and they were the scum of creation—had something more than justice. The Acting Provost pronounced sentence, which the priest translated, and a file of *mutilés* in the yard did the rest.

"If the Boches get in here we'll pay for this day's work," said the judge cheerfully. "But I'll go easier to the grave for having got rid of those swine."

On the fourth day he had a sudden sense of dignity. He examined his apparel, and found it very bad. He needed a new bonnet, a new kilt, and puttees, and he would be the better with a new shirt. Being aware that commandeering for personal use ill suited his office, he put the case before the Procureur, and a *Commission de Ravitaillement* was appointed. Shirts and puttees were easily got, but the kilt and bonnet were difficulties. But next morning Mam'selle Omèrine brought a gift. It was a bonnet with such a dicing round the rim as no Jock ever wore, and a skirt—it is the truest word—of that pattern which graces the persons of small girls in France. It was not the Lennox tartan, it was not any kind of tartan, but Private Galbraith did not laugh. He accepted the garments with a stammer of thanks, and, what is more, he put them on. The Ypriotes saw his splendor with approval. It was a proof of his new frame of mind that he did not even trouble to reflect what his comrades would think of his costume, and that he kissed the bonnet affectionately before he went to bed.

That night he had evil dreams. He suddenly saw the

upshot of it all—himself degraded and shot as a deserter, and his brief glory pricked like a bubble. Grim forebodings of a court-martial assailed him. What would Mam'selle think of him when he was led away in disgrace—he who for a little had been a king? He walked about the floor in a frenzy of disquiet, and stood long at the window peering over the *Place,* lit by a sudden blink of moonlight. It could never be, he decided. Something desperate would happen first. The crash of a shell a quarter of a mile off reminded him that he was in the midst of war—war with all its chances of cutting knots.

Next morning no Procureur appeared. Then came the priest with a sad face and a sadder tale. Mam'selle had been out late the night before on an errand of mercy, and a shell, crashing through a gable, had sent an avalanche of masonry into the street. She was dead, without pain, said the priest, and in the sure hope of Heaven.

The others wept, but Private Galbraith strode from the room, and in a very little time was at the house of the Procureur. He saw his little colleague laid out for death after the fashion of her church, and his head suddenly grew very clear and his heart hotter than fire.

"I must resign this job," he told the Committee of Public Safety. "I've been forgetting that I'm a soldier and not a provost. It's my duty to get a nick at those Boches."

They tried to dissuade him, but he was adamant. His rule was over, and he was going back to serve.

But he was not allowed to resign. For that afternoon, after a week's absence, the British troops came again into Ypres.

They found a decorous little city, and many people who spoke of *le Roi*—which they assumed to signify the good King Albert. Also, in a corner of the cathedral yard, sitting disconsolately on the edge of a fallen monument, Company

Sergeant-Major Macvittie of the 3rd Lennox Highlanders found Private Peter Galbraith.

"My God, Galbraith, you've done it this time! *You'll* catch it in the neck! Absent for a week without leave, and getting yourself up to look like Harry Lauder! You come along with me!"

"I'll come quiet," said Galbraith with strange meekness. He was wondering how to spell Omèrine St. Marais, in case he wanted to write it in his Bible.

The events of the next week were confusing to a plain man. Galbraith was very silent, and made no reply to the chaff with which at first he was greeted. Soon his fellows forbore to chaff him, regarding him as a doomed man who had come well within the pale of the ultimate penalties.

He was examined by his commanding officer, and interviewed by still more exalted personages. The story he told was so bare as to be unintelligible. He asked for no mercy, and gave no explanations. But there were other witnesses besides him—the priest, for example, and Monsieur St. Marais, in a sober suit of black and very dark under the eyes.

By-and-by the court gave its verdict. Private Peter Galbraith was found guilty of riding roughshod over the king's regulations; he had absented himself from his battalion without permission; he had neglected his own duties and usurped without authority a number of superior functions; he had been the cause of the death or maltreatment of various persons who, whatever their moral deficiencies, must be regarded for the purposes of the case as civilian allies. The court, however, taking into consideration the exceptional circumstances in which Private Galbraith had been placed, inflicted no penalty and summarily discharged the prisoner.

Privately, his commanding officer and the still more exalted personages shook hands with him, and told him that he was a devilish good fellow and a credit to the British Army.

But Peter Galbraith cared for none of these things. As he sat again in the trenches at Saint Eloi, in six inches of water and a foot of mud, he asked his neighbor how many Germans were opposite them.

"I was hearing that there was maybe fifty thousand," was the answer.

Private Galbraith was content. He thought that the whole fifty thousand would scarcely atone for the death of one slim, dark-eyed girl.

First Patrol

BY CHARLES NORDHOFF AND
JAMES NORMAN HALL

My first day at the squadron chanced to be a rainy one,
when all the pilots were at mess together. In days of good
weather we ate more or less irregularly, for patrols came
first and meals afterward. There were twelve noncommis-
sioned officers in our mess, a gay, hearty crowd who made

me feel at home at once. Laguesse introduced me all around while Felix was putting the food on the table; then we sat down.

Sergeant Fontana, *chef de popote,* occupied the head of the table. He was a bluff ex-infantryman from southern France, a man with an enormous appetite and what seemed to me a depraved love for garlic. Every day at lunch Felix placed beside his plate a huge spud of garlic, a gift sent to him regularly by his mother from their home in Arles.

On Fontana's right sat Marcantoni, a swarthy little Corsican whom everyone called Napoleon. He bubbled over with good spirits and was popular with everyone, particularly with Fontana, who hung on every word he said and laughed at some of his witticisms till the tears rolled down his cheeks. "Did you hear what little Napoleon just said?" he would roar to the others at the end of the table. "Marc, after the war you've got to come to Arles; I'll never be able to live without you."

The other men nearest me were Adjutant Masson, Sergeant Volokoff, a Russian from the Foreign Legion, and Sergeant Golasse.

Golasse was the smallest man in the squadron, so short, in fact, that he had to have a special cushion made for the seat of his Spad so that his head could be brought up to the level of his windshield. He was a Parisian, and very proud of the fact. He knew all the wartime songs of the boulevards, and his talk was so full of slang that at first I had difficulty in understanding him. Before the war he had been a taxicab driver. He had joined the squadron only two months before my arrival after three years in the infantry, and had already shot down two enemy planes.

What a contrast he made to Volokoff, who was six feet three, an aristocratic, strikingly handsome man, and the only silent member of the mess. He had had the unusual distinction of winning the Legion of Honor in the Infantry as a noncom. A good many commissioned officers have the decoration, but when one sees the red ribbon on the breast of a corporal or sergeant one can be sure that it is for some deed of exceptional merit—such a deed as wins the V. C. in the British Army or the Congressional Medal in the American Service. What Volokoff had done to win it none of the mess knew, for he never spoke of his past military service or of his past life. I think he was the most melancholy man, when sober, I have ever met. He drank a great deal of brandy, was a wonderful guitar player, and spoke English, French, and German with equal ease. The only time when he could be called talkative was when the conversation turned to Germany and her responsibility for the war. He hated Germans, individually and collectively, and it was the dream of his life to shoot down an enemy plane. He was recklessly brave, but such a poor flier and such a bad shot that he had had no luck thus far. He crashed more planes than all the other members of the squadron together, and his Spad was always getting riddled in the air.

Much of this, of course, I learned later. At my first meal, I merely listened to the talk, making mental notes of my impressions of the various pilots. Scarcely a reference was made to flying or fighting. Rainy days were like schoolboys' holidays—little breathing spells between periods of work —and anyone who mentioned work was immediately sat on.

But the holiday came to an abrupt end in the very middle of it. Felix had just brought the dessert—stewed pears and cake—and was going round filling the coffee cups when an orderly from Group Headquarters appeared. The moment he stuck in his head he was greeted with howls and execrations and bombarded with pieces of bread. Golasse and Marcantoni sprang up and danced around him, shooing him off with their napkins. "*Va-t'en! Va-t'en!* Get out this minute! What are you doing here on a rainy day? Don't you dare tell us there's a patrol this afternoon! Man, it's impossible to fly! Look at the sky!"

The orderly leaned against the doorjamb, folded his arms, and waited.

"Well, *look* at the sky," he said. "Then maybe you'll understand why I'm here. I didn't make the weather. If you must blame someone, blame *le bon Dieu*. All I know is that this squadron has two patrols to furnish and you're to take off in twenty minutes." With that he went to the bulletin board and tacked up the orders.

The messroom windows were fitted with ground glass like that used in factory windows at home. Not being able to see through them, we had not noticed that the rain had stopped and that the clouds were lifting a little. The pilots crowded around the bulletin board, gulping their coffee as they read the orders. The squadron was to furnish two patrols, one of eight planes to fly below the clouds, covering the sector on the east side of the salient as far south as Saint-Mihiel. The order that set my pulse to beating faster read as follows:

High patrol—4500 meters to 5500 meters. Sector: Varennes-Etain. Sergeant Laguesse, Sergeant Volokoff, Corporal Selden.

Laguesse put his hand on my shoulder. "Good, Selden! I'm glad we're going out together for your first time over." He looked at his wrist watch. "One forty-five. We must be getting off."

The hangars of the squadron were a five-minutes' walk

from our barracks. The flying field was soggy after the rain, and we squashed along in our wooden shoes, which all French pilots wore in such weather when going to and from the airfield. The sky was lightening perceptibly and the cloud ceiling was now at about two thousand meters. Off to the northeast was a small patch of blue sky, the yellow sunlight streaming through it in a wide shaft.

"We'll go up through that hole, eh, Volokoff?" said Laguesse. "Chances are we won't even see the ground after we get up. It'll be a nice quiet promenade. Well, it will give Selden a chance to try out his *coucou*."

"Lucky dogs!" said Golasse, who was walking with us. "Now why couldn't I have been slated for high patrol today? Look at those clouds! Neither too high nor too low for the Archie gunners! We'll be right underneath, as plain as flies on a white ceiling. One thing's sure, the low patrol is going to be shelled to blazes!"

"*Sacré chameau!*" said Fontana. "What's the use of sending us out merely to be shot at?"

"Listen to the ancient senator from Arles!" said Laguesse jubilantly. "My poor old garlic-eating friend, it's to make you agile in the air. You're too slow and leisurely in your movements—in other words, too fat. That old Spad of yours is getting fat too. Well, you'd better look sharp today when the one-hundred-and-fives are growling round you! Otherwise we'll be electing a new *chef de popote*. By the way, have you brought your garlic with you? There's none in Germany, you know, and what will you do in a German prison camp without your garlic?"

Our Spads were drawn up in beautiful alignment in front of the hangars. The mechanics already had the engines warmed up, and propellers were idling over at 350 revolutions. It was always a thrilling sound to me to hear the gentle rhythmical purring of powerful motors just before patrol time; it seemed to give a voice to one's own feeling of excitement at the moment when pilots were hastily jumping into their flying clothes, buttoning their combination suits, fastening the chin straps of their helmets, putting on their gloves. It was hard to realize at such times that a few moments later we should be miles distant from our quiet flying field, seeking battle among the clouds or far in the depths of blue sky. Even at this distance of time and place, the mere thought of those days makes the pulses leap and brings a tightening to the muscles of the throat.

There was no dallying now, no further expressions of regret that there was work to be done. Everyone was eager to be off. One mechanic stood by each plane, ready to jerk the chocks from under the wheels the moment the signal was given. The pilots slid down into their tiny seats and armed their machine guns; the second mechanics mounted the step to give a final polish to the windshield and to help fasten the buckles of the seat straps. The low patrol was to leave the field first. Captain Clermont was already in his bus. He tried out his controls, gave his motor full gas for a few seconds; the little plane quivered and pushed with all her strength against the chocks. Then he looked at his wrist watch and nodded to his mechanic. The chocks were jerked out; he taxied across the field and turned into the wind. The other pilots of his patrol followed in single file, and a moment later they were climbing swiftly toward their rendezvous over the village of Brizeaux, a few miles distant in the direction of Verdun.

The high patrol left immediately after, on the very stroke of two. Laguesse was leading, then Volokoff and I. We were to meet at a thousand meters over the field. I tried out my motor, pulling the throttle wide open while I watched the revolution counter. The indicator leaped swiftly—1500, 1750, 1800. It was glorious music the engine made, deep and powerful, sweet and clear, without a suspicion of a false note. Cartier clung to the side of the fuselage with both hands, bending his head against the blast of cold air from the propeller. When I reduced again he sprang on the step for a second and clapped me on the back.

"*Çá gaze*, eh?" he shouted in my ear. "Keep your eyes peeled! Good luck!"

I taxied out after Volokoff, swung round into the wind, and as I gave her free rein again my Spad lifted her tail, skimmed along the ground, and rose swiftly into the air. I had such confidence in her and was so elated to think that I was really off for my first patrol that I did a foolish thing— something that young and silly airmen were often doing. When not fifty feet from the ground I zoomed up in a steep climbing turn. My little bus responded beautifully. If she had not—well, there, very likely, would have been the end of both our careers. How many young airmen, I wonder, are sleeping in graves overseas merely because they wished to show off as they were leaving the ground—to do something "houndish," as we used to say? Scores of them, hundreds of them. One never saw an old and experienced pilot tempting fate needlessly. He waited until he was at a safe distance from old Mother Earth before trying any monkey tricks.

I climbed steadily for half a minute, then turned back toward the airfield. Off to the northeast the planes of the low patrol were taking height over Brizeaux; they looked like a tiny swarm of gnats. Below me I saw the mechanics standing in a group in front of the hangars. Each of them would be talking of the qualities of his particular Spad, and the faults and virtues of his particular pilot. They were a keenly critical lot, those French *mécanos*, connoisseurs of flying, and as outspoken as they were critical. To be highly praised by one's own mechanics was an experience to be remembered.

At a thousand meters a plane with a blue stripe running the length of the upper wings passed me, made a steep bank to the right, and headed north. That was Laguesse. Volokoff and I dropped in behind and we climbed toward the break in the clouds we had seen from below.

The opening seemed to have been made for our benefit, for it had considerably widened within a quarter of an hour; but the moment we had climbed through, it closed again, and we had below us an unbroken sea of clouds as far as the eye could reach in every direction. But now, overhead, was nothing but blue sky, a deep autumnal blue, and the air was so clear that it seemed to have washed the very sunlight from a rich gold to the palest yellow. It gave me a feeling of exhilaration to be flying in that lonely upper world, knowing that the earth was wrapped in gray gloom. One seemed no longer to belong to earth, to have no further concern with what might be taking place there.

For five minutes or more we flew steadily northward, skimming along just over the floor of cloud. It gave one the same sense of speed that flying close to the ground does. At times I could imagine that we were hanging motionless and that it was the clouds that moved, streaming under us at a terrific rate. Here and there they billowed up in almost vertical columns of mist, dazzling white in the sunshine. Sometimes Laguesse, who was about a hundred meters in advance, would zoom over these—cloud-steeple-chasing, we called it—and sometimes dash straight through, his propeller churning them up and raveling them out in shreds of silky vapor; while Volokoff and I, following in his wake, would feel the cool moisture on our faces, beading our eyebrows and the little hairs on our cheekbones. Below us, and a little to the right, three lonely shadows of planes moved at incredible speed over a sea of foam.

For the moment I had quite forgotten that there was a war in progress; that there were such things as German aircraft—in fact, I had all but lost the sense of my own identity. I felt like a disembodied spirit that had escaped all the trials and tribulations of earthly existence and had nothing more to do forever except to roam at will over limitless meadows of cloud.

Of a sudden Laguesse brought me back—I can't say to earth, but to present consciousness—by rocking his plane horizontally. I knew what that meant. It was the patrol leader's signal: "Look out! Enemy planes!" Volokoff and I were flying wing to wing and not more than thirty yards apart. He waved and pointed upward to the right. I looked, but saw nothing. Laguesse made a bank to the left and started climbing. The needle of my altimeter began to move slowly—2500 meters, 2800, 3000, 3200. I kept searching the sky, directly overhead, to the left and right, and to the rear, but still I saw only the great dome of blue, immaculate, lonely, seemingly empty. We turned northward again and held that course for a time. Soon we were at 5000 meters and the floor of cloud was farther below us than it had been above when we left the ground. Still no sign of a Boche. I was getting exasperated, and for a moment the suspicion crossed my mind that Laguesse and Volokoff were having a little game with me because I was a green pilot. But that was only for a moment. Of a sudden I saw that the air was filled with planes.

While in training in the schools I had often tried to imagine what my first air battle would be like. I haven't a very fertile imagination, and in my mental picture of such a battle I had seen planes approaching one another more or less deliberately, their guns spitting fire, then turning to spit again. That, in fact, is what happens, except that the approach is anything but deliberate once the engagement starts. But where I had been chiefly mistaken was in thinking of them fighting at a considerable distance from each other—two, or three, or even five hundred yards.

The reality was far different. At the instant when I found myself surrounded with planes, I heard unmistakably the crackle of machine-gun fire. It is curious how different this sounds in the air when one's ears are deafened by altitude, the rush of wind, and the roar of the motor. Even when quite close it is only a faint crackle, but very distinct, each explosion impinging sharply on the eardrums. I turned my head over my shoulder, to breathe the acrid smoke of tracer bullets, and just then—whang! crash! —my windshield was shattered. I made a steep bank in time to see the black crosses of a silver-bellied Albatross turn up horizontally about twenty yards distant, as though the German pilot merely wanted to display them to convince me that he was really a German. Then, as I leveled off, glancing hastily to the right, I saw not ten meters below my altitude and flying in the same direction a craft that looked enormous, larger than three of mine. She had staggered wings, and there was no doubt about the insignia on the fishlike tail: that too was a black cross. It was a two-seater, and so close that I could clearly see the pilot and the gunner in the back seat. Body and wings were camouflaged, not in daubs after the French fashion, but in zigzag lines of brown and green. The observer, whose back was toward me, was aiming two guns mounted on a single swivel on the circular tract surrounding his cockpit. He crouched down, firing at a steep angle at someone overhead whom I could not see, his tracers stabbing through the air in thin clear lines. Apparently neither the pilot nor the rear gunner saw me. Then I had a blurred glimpse of the tricolor *cocardes* of a Spad that passed me like a flash, going in the opposite direction; and in that same instant I saw another Spad appear directly under the two-seater, nose up vertically, and seem to hang there as though suspended by an invisible wire.

What then happened is beyond the power of any words of mine to describe. A sheet of intense flame shot up from the two-seater, lapping like water around the wings and blown back along the body of the plane. The observer dropped his guns and I could all but see the expression of horror on his face as he turned. He ducked for a second with his arms around his head in an effort to protect himself; then without a moment's hesitation he climbed on his seat and threw himself off into space. The huge plane veered up on one side, turned nose down, and disappeared beneath me. Five seconds later I was alone. There wasn't another plane to be seen.

This, I realize, is a very sketchy account of my first air battle, but I am telling here, not all that happened, but merely what I saw. As for what I felt, I had time for only two sensations: first, astonishment at the sudden appearance of all those planes and to find my windshield shattered; second, horror as I saw the German plane go down and the rear gunner hurl himself into the air; then another shock of surprise at finding myself alone.

The fight was over, of course, in much less time than it takes to tell of it. I don't believe twenty-five seconds elapsed between the time when I first heard the crackle of machine-gun fire and the second when the two-seater vanished beneath me. I banked steeply to the right and left; I flew in circles, looking in every direction, mystified, completely at a loss to know what had happened to everyone.

And I was ashamed too because of my air blindness. "Lord!" I thought. "I'll never make a pursuit pilot. I'll never find anything to pursue." What seemed most astonishing was that a huge German two-seater, wrapped in flame, could fall without my seeing how and where it fell. But I could still see, and smell too, the cloud of oily black smoke it had left behind, and the thin straight lines of smoke left by tracer bullets, crisscrossing in the air, now raveling out in the wind. A sense of the unreality of the adventure came over me as I circled round them, looking at these faint vanishing evidences of combat. Had it happened? Shouldn't I wake up in a moment and find that I had dreamed it? Then for the first time I remembered my own machine gun. I hadn't fired a shot—I had not even thought of firing!

All this time I had been flying round and round, quite unconscious of direction or anything else except a feeling of bitter disappointment that I had been so helpless, so useless in my first air battle. No doubt many young airmen had similar experiences during their early days at the front. The trouble was, of course, that one's brain still functioned in the old leisurely way, and, when confronted with wholly new and strange conditions calling for immediate decisions and immediate action, all that it could do—in my case at any rate—was to register astonishment.

How strange these conditions were was brought home to me as I came out of my reverie with a start and looked at my clock. In every plane there was a small clock fastened to the instrument board in front of the pilot's seat among the other dials: the pressure gauge, altimeter, tachometer, gasoline gauge, and so forth. They were set by squadron time before every patrol. Looking at mine, I saw that it was twenty-three minutes after two. I didn't believe it, and looked again. Twenty-three minutes after two; and the clock was unquestionably running, the second hand making its leisurely sixty-beat circuit.

It seemed impossible that only half an hour before I had been walking out to the hangars with Laguesse. We were to patrol the sector until four o'clock—an hour and a half to go. I didn't mind that, but I did mind having lost Laguesse and Volokoff and not knowing where I was. We were to cover the sector between Varennes and Etain, the north side of the Verdun Salient, but as to where they were—or Verdun, or Sénard, for that matter—I had only the vaguest of notions. Thinking back over the direction we had taken from the airfield, the turns we had made, and the length of time we had been flying, I decided that I must be somewhere over the Argonne, so I turned eastward. But I was a bit uneasy, knowing that my reckoning was probably wrong. If it was out and I was farther to the east, then I might be flying into Germany toward Diedenhofen or some such place. The floor of cloud still covered everything; not a break anywhere.

I throttled down my motor, just keeping flying speed, looking out sharply for Germans. But the sky was empty save for my little plane. I had just convinced myself of this when directly in front of me a Spad materialized out of thin air and passed over me diagonally, upside down in an Immelmann turn, as though it were being swept along by a wind blowing at hurricane speed. What a welcome sight those tricolor *cocardes* were! I turned at once to follow this airman and found that he was turning to have another look at me. We passed so close that I could see his plane insignia. On the side of the fuselage there was a red swastika, and beside it the Indian-head insignia of the Lafayette Escadrille.

What in the world is he doing at this part of the line?

I wondered. The Lafayette Squadron was at Chaudun on the Aisne, flying the Chemin des Dames sector, or had been when last I heard of them. For a moment I thought this pilot might be Bill O'Connor, flying down to Sénard to have a yarn with Gordon and me, but I immediately discarded this possibility. O'Connor, like myself, was an average pilot, and I knew that he couldn't fly as this man flew. I had never seen, except when Tommy Slater was in the air, more precise or beautiful maneuvering. After a leisurely examination of my Spad, he waved his hand as though in farewell and started off in a northerly direction.

But if he meant it to be farewell, I, at least, did not. I knew instinctively that he wasn't lost; the movements of his Spad convinced me that both of them knew what they were about. So I tagged along behind, very glad of company, and resolved to land wherever he did, even though it were somewhere on the Aisne front. He soon observed me following him and again waved his hand, as much as to say, "Coming along? All right; we'll finish the patrol together." We were flying at about 5000 meters, but presently his bus began to rise swiftly, in the odd way which gives one behind the curious impression that his own plane is unaccountably sinking. He had started to climb, of course, so I climbed after him.

A first-class 180 Spad in perfect condition had a ceiling of 6000 meters, and sometimes they could climb as high as 6200. I was keenly interested to see what my little ship could do, so I followed my unknown companion, resolved to climb, or to try to climb, as long as he did. At 5900 I passed him; then we both managed to reach 6000; then I rose above him again by 100 meters. He reached up a hand as though he meant to say, "Give me a lift, will you?" Six thousand was the best he could do, and 6100 was the limit of my Spad, and she was very wobbly at that height.

But I was more than satisfied. Never had I flown so high before. Six thousand one hundred! I thought. Nearly twenty thousand feet! Not many of the world's mountains were as high as that.

We came down again to 5000 and turned west, I still keeping about 100 meters behind. I didn't worry much now about missing anything. I felt certain that if there was anything to be seen my companion would see it. It gave me a keen pleasure to watch him fly—he was so sure of every movement and seemed to make them as naturally as a fish swims. He loafed along, doing Immelmann turns, loops, and barrel turns, and I did clumsy imitations. I was glad he wasn't watching me. Nevertheless, I was having a thoroughly good time, and it gave a zest to this patrol not to know where we were or where I should have supper that night.

We flew high for another hour in a lonely sky, eastward and then westward again, while the sun dropped toward the cloud floor. At last my companion tipped up and dived so steeply that I lost him for a moment; but I had my wits about me now and soon made him out, far below, descending in steep spirals. I followed, at first believing that he had sighted some Germans, but just before reaching the clouds he leveled out again and flew quietly on, winding here and there among deep ravines of mist now filled with blue and purple shadow in the light of the sinking sun. It was a glorious sight to see those clouds stained more and more deeply with color, but I was prevented from thoroughly enjoying it because of the difficulty I had in keeping my companion in sight. Occasionally he would vanish; then, passing a great promontory, I would catch sight of him again banking steeply around a distant cloud castle, his Spad looking microscopic under those towering bastions, and I would speed after him, the roar of my motor reverberating faintly against walls of shining vapor. Suddenly he did a loop, and, instead of pulling up in line of flight, he went on down and disappeared in the clouds.

I followed, of course, and thought I should never reach clear air again. When I did, what a contrast to the sunny air above! It seemed almost dark on the ground, but my eyes soon became accustomed to the gray light, and I had the good fortune to find my patrol companion almost at once. He was circling round as though waiting for me, and the moment I joined him turned south, holding a steady course. Beneath us was a vast stretch of forest land, looking very gloomy in the fading light. I had lost all sense of direction above the clouds, and I thought it likely that this was the Forest of Villers-Cotterets, on the Aisne front, and that we should soon be landing at the airfield of the Escadrille Lafayette. Then I had another of my many surprises on this day. I found another Spad flying alongside me, and the insignia on the fuselage was that of a black cat, spitting. I made a climbing turn to pass over it, and the pilot's insignia was the long blue stripe of Laguesse. A moment later, looking down over the side, I saw the hangars of Sénard.

Years seemed to have elapsed since last I had seen that field. I felt as Columbus must have felt when he returned from his first voyage to the Indies. For mine too had been a voyage of discovery, with this difference in the circumstances, that I did all my discovering after the voyage was over. By good luck I made a beautiful landing and taxied up to the hangars feeling as proud as though I had gained a dozen victories. Cartier and Vigneau were waiting for me. I climbed down stiffly. Cartier was speaking, and for a moment I couldn't hear a word he said, my ears had been so deafened by changing altitudes; but after swallowing a few times and holding my nose, blowing through the ear passages, they were suddenly cleared. Then his voice sounded unusually distinct.

". . . *comme un papillon!*" he was saying. "That's the way to land. I couldn't tell when your wheels touched the ground. Well, how's the little ship? Does she fly? Any trouble with—" He broke off abruptly, put his hands on his hips, and stood regarding me with pursed lips and a series of solemn nods. "One wound stripe for the old combination," he said. "Well, you've seen a Boche, that's sure; at any rate, he saw you."

Following his gaze, I saw that the left shoulder of my combination suit had been cut through as neatly as though it had been done with a knife. I was about to tell him about my shattered windshield when he mounted the step and discovered it for himself; and he found that another bullet had ripped the fabric on the side of the fuselage.

"That bird was after you, Selden! What did you do to *him*, if it's fair to ask?"

"Cartier, don't say a word! I didn't even see him till after he fired, and I was so surprised that I didn't remember I had a gun!"

A little knot of mechanics had gathered around my plane, and Vigneau was exhibiting the bullet marks as though they were valuable curiosities; for the French mechanics seemed almost as proud of their pilots when they brought home scars as when they brought victories.

Off to the west the clouds were breaking up, and the sun, very low, appeared through the trees, flooding the field with rosy light, casting long shadows over the wet smooth-shaven turf. The wind had died away and the wind sleeves on the hangars hung limp on their poles. A dozen or more Spads were circling over the airfield awaiting turns to land, for, beside the patrols of our squadron, formations had gone out from the other squadrons. The air was filled with the throbbing of motors and the whistling sound of planes coming down, and high overhead I saw three ships, their wings gleaming in the sunset light, losing altitude in spirals and serpentines.

The airfield was always a scene of great animation when the last patrols for the day were coming in. Off-duty airmen strolled out from barracks to hear the news, and both pilots and mechanics gathered about the planes as they taxied up to the hangars. Here some birdman, usually a young one, would be sitting on the back of his ship, his goggles pushed up on his helmet, describing a combat with eloquent gestures; farther along another would be standing on his seat, pounding his shoulders with his hands to get the blood into circulation after his long flight. Often the men were so numb with cold that they had difficulty in getting out of their flying clothes, and would stand stiffly, like tailors' dummies, while their mechanics unbuttoned them and removed their flying boots.

I was still talking with Cartier when someone slapped me on the shoulder. It was Laguesse. "Now then," he said, "give an account of yourself! Where have *you* been all this while? You might give me a cigarette while you're explaining. You owe me at least one for pulling that Boche off your back."

"Did you do that?"

"Of course! Didn't you see me?"

I shook my head. I decided that I might as well make a clean breast of it and confess how very little I had seen.

Laguesse listened quietly until I had finished. "Well," he said, "I don't know what kind of *porte-bonheur* you carry, but whatever it is, keep it. It's a good one." Then he laughed. "But don't worry. You'll soon get your eye in. I was just as blind when I first joined the squadron, and just as bewildered, too, in my first scrap."

Then he told me what had happened. There were by no means as many planes in the fracas as I had imagined: only three German ships, in fact—the two-seater and two Albatross single-seaters; our own patrol of three, and a lone Spad that joined up from the other side at the moment of the fight.

"They were at 5000 when I first spotted them," he went on, "heading southeast across the salient. They didn't seem to be in a hurry, and just after I signaled you they turned back north. That's why I turned west when we started to climb. Apparently they had not spotted us, and I wanted to keep in the sun. I don't believe they saw us until we were nearly on their level and about half a mile away; then they made straight for us. Whether they spotted that lone Spad coming down on them from the east, I don't know, but I think they must have. Pity for the two-seater he didn't know who was flying that *coucou!*"

"Was that the Spad with the Indian head and the swastika?"

"Yes. Didn't you see that?"

"I saw the plane, but I didn't have time then to examine his insignia."

"Neither did those Germans. Did you ever see prettier work? Luf came up from behind, stood on his tail for two seconds, and fired one burst. Good-by, Fritz! Poor devils! A horrible sight, wasn't it? I saw the pilot fall over on his stick; he was evidently hit, but the observer wasn't. I take my hat off to that chap! It takes nerve to jump out of a plane at 5000 meters. Of course, it was certain death to stay —he would have been burned to a cinder—but just the same I doubt whether I should have had the courage to jump. By the way, that's Luf's thirteenth victory."

"Luf? You don't mean Raoul Lufbery, do you?"

"Now who else could I mean? How many Lufberys are there in the French Air Service?"

"Why, I've been flying with him! I met him after I lost you and Volokoff. I was with him all the rest of the patrol!"

"Well, that's nothing to your discredit. You couldn't have been with a better man, especially on your first patrol. Hello! There's Luf now. He's a great friend of the Captain. That's how he happened to be down our way today; he was coming over for a visit when we all had that happy meeting over the Argonne. Hey, Luf!"

The next moment he was introducing me, and I felt as proud as Lucifer. There would be a story for my grandchildren if ever I had any—my first patrol and my first battle in company with Lieutenant Lufbery, the best pilot in the Lafayette Flying Corps, and among the best in the entire French Air Service.

Lufbery smiled and held out his hand. "Selden? Oh, yes, I've heard your friend O'Connor speak of you. So it was you I was flying with, was it?"

I thought that a very kind way to put it when the fact was so unquestionably the other way round. I had been flying with him, hanging on to his tail like a little lost boy to a kind policeman's hand. "But how in the world did you know where we were?" I asked. "Lord knows where I should have landed if I hadn't met you."

He laughed. "Oh, I had all the clouds marked. You must always do that when you can't see the ground. That is a fine little ship of yours. She can climb! By the way, Laguesse, what happened to that Albatross you pried loose from Selden's tail?"

"He dived just after you bagged the two-seater, and he must have gone down full motor. Never saw a ship fade so fast. I didn't float down by any means, but he was a good three hundred meters ahead when he ducked into the clouds. I ducked after him, but I couldn't find him again. Then I picked up a crowd from another squadron and played round with them."

"What became of Volokoff?" I asked.

Laguesse laughed nervously. "He was having a little private war with that other Albatross the last I saw of him. Don't know what happened. All I do know is that he isn't back yet."

Just then Sergeant Fontana, who had been on the low patrol, joined us. Laguesse greeted him jovially. "Well, my ancient senatorial friend! You didn't— What is it, old man?" he added quietly.

"Marcantoni's gone. What a beast of a war!" Then he sat down on a gasoline tin and began to cry like a child.

No one spoke for a moment. The other pilots of the low patrol were coming down the field. Lufbery walked over and shook hands silently with Captain Clermont. They stood in a little group, looking helplessly at Sergeant Fontana, as though all of them were wishing they could cry like that.

"The poor little devil! Little Napoleon! And we've been bunking together since—"

Captain Clermont nodded to us to come away. "Let him have it out alone. Luf, I've just heard about your two-seater. Bully for you, old man!"

Laguesse, Golasse, and I were walking behind. "How did it happen, Golasse?"

"It was north of Brabant, over the Meuse. We met a gang of Albatross. Little Napoleon got it right at the start. He was killed—no doubt of that. Crashed in a wood near Dannevoux, where the river makes that loop to the west. They were a mordant lot, that crowd!"

"Just the same, honors were even," Masson added. "The

captain knocked one down. That Boche didn't know what hit him."

"I saw him crash. It must have been about a quarter of a mile from where little Marc fell."

"My gun jammed, and I couldn't clear it. Had to fly the whole patrol without a gun!"

"That's some battery, north of Etain! They were certainly sticking them close!"

Volokoff came in the next day. His Spad had been so badly shot up by the second Albatross that he had been compelled to land near Sainte-Menehould.

Dinner that evening was a very noisy one. Everyone talked at once; Golasse cracked his funniest jokes, and the squadron phonograph was never allowed to stop for a moment. I have never seen a more gallant or a less successful attempt to drown the eloquence of one empty chair.

Sherlock Nobody Holmes

BY PERCY K. FITZHUGH

When Archibald Archer, steward's boy on the Atlantic liner, *Warrington,* offered to get Tom Slade a job on board the ship, Tom was highly elated, and could hardly wait for Saturday to come. Saturday was the day on which Archer's shore leave expired.

"I'm sick and tired of fooling around here, and helping the Home Defencers," Tom had said to his friend. "If I was eighteen I'd enlist. . . ."

"Why don't you *say* you're eighteen?" said Archer. "They'd never know the diff. Lots of fellows have got in by saying they're older than they really are."

"I promised my scoutmaster I wouldn't try to enlist until

I'm eighteen," said Tom, sulkily. "You can bet I won't wait a day over that, though! I want to get somewhere where there's a chance of some adventure."

"Well, I don't know what you call adventure," said Archer, "but if they take you aboard the *Warrington,* you stand a good chance of being torpedoed, if that'll satisfy you."

This was beyond Tom's wildest dreams.

So on Saturday they went to the city together and walked along the water front until they came to the dock where the *Warrington* lay.

The steamship company, aided and abetted by Uncle Sam, had enshrouded the whole prosy business of loading and sailing with a delightful covering of romance, and Tom Slade realized, as he and young Archer approached the sacred precincts, that the departure of a vessel today is quite as much fraught with perilous and adventurous possibilities as was the sailing of a Spanish galleon in the good old days of yore.

A high board fence protected the pier from public gaze and as Tom read the glaring recruiting posters which decorated it he felt that, even if he wasn't old enough to enlist, he was at last about to do something worthwhile— something which would involve the risk of his life.

By a little door in the big fence sat a man on a stool. Two other men near him eyed the boys shrewdly.

"First barbed-wire entanglement," said Archer, as they approached. "Keep your mouth shut, but if you have to answer any questions tell them the truth. They're spotters."

"What?" said Tom, a little uneasy.

"Secret-service men—they can tell if your great-grandfather was German."

"He wasn't," said Tom.

"Hello, old spiff-head," called Archer to the gatekeeper,

setting down his satchel with an air of having done the same thing before. The secret-service men opened it and rummaged its contents, one helping himself to an apple.

"You blooming grafter," said Archibald.

"That's all right, Archie," said the other man, likewise helping himself. "Who's your friend?"

"He's going in to see the steward," said Archer. "I told him I'd get a feller for the butcher. . . ."

"All the passes are taken up," said the gateman, as he took Archer's pass. "Everybody's on board and there's nobody needed."

"Oh, is that so?" said Archer, derisively. "Just because everybody's on board it don't prove nobody's needed."

"He'll only come back out again," said the gatekeeper.

"Oh, will he?" said Archer, ironically.

"Let him in," said one of the secret-service men with a laugh, and as he spoke he pulled Tom's pockets inside out in a very perfunctory way and slapped his clothing here and there. It was evident that young Archer was a favorite. Tom felt very important.

"Didn't I tell you I was lucky?" Archer said, as he and Tom lugged the big valise down the pier. "But they're getting more careful all the time. Next sailing, maybe, when we're taking troops over, President Wilson himself couldn't get by with it."

Tom had never been in close proximity to an ocean steamer, even in peacetime, and the scene which now confronted him was full of interest. Along the side of the pier rose the great black bulk of the mighty ship. Up and down the steep gangways hurried men in uniform. Several soldiers in khaki strolled back and forth. Hanging from a mammoth crane was part of the framework of a great airplane. On the pier were several Red Cross ambulances and a big pile of stretchers; tremendous spools, fifteen feet or more in diameter, wound with barbed wire; heavy canvas-covered wagons, lettered *U.S.A.*, packed with poles and rolls of khaki-colored canvas; automobiles bearing the same initials, and shovels by the thousands, all similarly marked. There was no doubt that Uncle Sam was getting his sleeves rolled up for business.

At the foot of one of the gangways Archer had to open his bag again to gratify the curiosity of another man who, upon Archer's statement of Tom's errand, slapped Tom here and there in the vicinity of his pockets and said, "All right."

Archer led the way along the deck, down a companion-way and through a passage with doors marked *Surgeon, Chief Steward, Chief Engineer, First Mate*, etc. They entered the chief steward's cabin, where a man in uniform sat at a desk with other men standing all about, apparently awaiting orders. When his turn came, Archer said, "Do you remember, Mr. Cressey, you said you wished you had more youngsters like me in the steward's department? I got you one here. He's a friend of mine. He's just like me—only different. Tom Slade his name is, and he wants a job. He'd like to be chief engineer, but if he can't be that. . . ."

"Maybe he'd be willing to be butcher's assistant," concluded the steward. "Archer," he added, as he reached for one of several speaking tubes near his desk, "if I thought you'd sink I'd have you thrown overboard. How'd you enjoy your visit home?"

A brief talk with some unseen person, to which Tom listened with chill misgivings, and the steward directed his young subordinate to take Tom to the purser's office and, if he got through all right there, to the ship's butcher. He gave Tom a slip of paper to hand to the purser.

It was to the third purser that Tom told the history of his life, so far as he knew it: where he was born and when, who his parents were, where they had been born, when and where they had died, whether Tom had ever worked on a ship, whether he had any relatives born or living in Germany or Austria, whether he had ever been employed by a German, and so on and so on.

All this went down in the big book, in which Tom had a page all to himself, and the last question left a chill upon him as he followed his young companion from the cabin— *Whom to notify in case of accident.*

Accident, he thought. That means torpedoing.

But against this was the glad news that for the round trip of presumably a month, he would receive one hundred and sixty dollars, forty dollars payable on arrival in a "foreign port," the balance "on return to an American port."

There would be no call upon this stupendous sum, save what he chose to spend in the mysterious, unknown foreign port, and Tom felt like the regular storybook hero who goes away under a cloud and comes back loaded with wealth and glory.

The butcher's domain was a long way below decks. The butcher himself was a genial soul who took Tom in hand without any ceremony. "Now I'll take you down," said he after preliminaries, "and show you the storerooms and refrigerators."

An iron ladder led down from the butcher's apartment to a dark passage, where he turned on an electric light. "Now these three doors," he said, "are to the three storerooms—one, two, three."

Tom followed him into one of the rooms. It was large, delightfully cool, and immaculately clean. All around were rows of shelves with screen doors before them, and here were stored canned goods—thousands upon thousands of cans, Tom would have said.

"You won't touch anything in here," his superior told

him. "None of this will be used before the return trip—maybe not then. Come in here."

Tom followed him through a passage from this room into another exactly like it. Along the passage were great ice-box doors. "Cold storage," his superior observed. "Now here's where you'll get your stuff. It's all alphabetical; if you want tomatoes, go to *T;* if you want salmon—*S.* Just like a dictionary. If I send you down for thirty pounds of salmon, that doesn't mean thirty cans—see?"

"Yes, sir," said Tom.

"Make up your thirty pounds of the biggest cans—a twenty and a ten. There's your opener," he added, pointing to a rather complicated mechanical can opener fastened to the bulkhead. "Open everything before you bring it up."

"Yes, sir."

He led Tom from one place to another, initiating him into the use of the chopping machine, the slicing machine, etc. "You won't find things very heavy this trip," he said, "but next trip we'll be feeding five thousand, maybe. Now's the time to go to school and learn. Here's the keys; you must always keep these places locked," he added, as he himself locked one of the doors for Tom. "They were just left open while they were being stocked. Now we'll go up."

That very night, when the great city was asleep, two tugboats, like a pair of sturdy little Davids, sidled up to the great steel Goliath, and slowly she moved out into midstream and turned her towering prow toward where the Goddess of Liberty held aloft her beckoning light in the vast darkness.

And Tom Slade was off upon his adventures.

Indeed, the first one had already occurred. He and Archer, having received intimations that the vessel might sail that night, had remained up to enjoy her stealthy nocturnal departure. They were leaning over the rail, watching the maneuvering of the tugs, when suddenly a man, carrying a suitcase, came running along the deck.

"We're not sailing, are we?" he asked excitedly as he passed.

"Looks that way," said Archer.

"Where's the gangway? Down that way?" the man asked, not waiting for an answer.

"He'll have a good big jump to the gangway," said Archer. "I guess he was asleep at the switch, hey? What d'you say we go down—just for the fun of it?"

"Come ahead," said Tom.

At the opening where the gangway had been, several men, including the excited passenger, were gathered. The rail had been drawn across the space and the ship was already a dozen feet or so from the wharf. Tom and Archer paused in the background, wisely inconspicuous.

"Certainly, you can't go ashore—how are you going to get ashore—jump?" asked an officer.

"You can have the gangway put up," insisted the man.

"You're talking nonsense," said the officer. "Can't you see we're out of reach and moving?"

"You'd only have to back her in a yard or two," said the man excitedly.

"What, the ship?" asked the officer in good-natured surprise, and several other men laughed.

"There's no use my starting without my apparatus!" said the passenger, his anger mounting. "It will be here tomorrow morning; it is promised! I was informed the ship would not sail before tomorrow night. This is an outrage. . . ."

"I'm sorry, sir," said the officer patiently. "The wharf closed this afternoon; notice was posted, sir."

"I saw no notice!" thundered the man. "It's of no use for

me to go without my belongings, I tell you! I cannot go! It is outrageous! I demand to be put ashore!"

By this time the vessel was in midstream, and his tirade was growing rather wearisome. Most of the bystanders sauntered away, laughing, and the two boys, seeing that nothing sensational was likely to happen, returned to the forward part of the ship.

"Do you think he was a German?" said Tom.

"No, sure he wasn't. Didn't you hear what good English he talked?"

"Yes, but he said *ah-par-ah-toos*," said Tom, "instead of *apparatus*. And he was sorry he said it, too, because the next time he said belongings."

"You make me laugh," said Archer.

"There's another thing that makes me think he's a German," said Tom, indifferent to Archer's scepticism.

"What's that?"

"He wanted the ship brought back just on his account."

Bucking the brisk morning breeze and holding on to his peaked service cap, Tom made his way along the deck next morning, bent on his new duties.

The door of the radio room was open as he passed, and the young operator was sitting back, with the receivers on his ears and his feet on the instrument shelf, eating a sandwich. "Hello, kiddo," said he.

Tom paused and looked about the cosy, shipshape little room with its big coil and its splendid, powerful instrument. "Do you live in here?" he asked.

"Nope," said the operator, "but I'm doing both shifts and I suppose I'll have to sleep right here with the claps on this trip."

"Isn't there another operator?" Tom asked.

"Yup—but he didn't show up."

Tom hesitated, not sure whether he ought to venture

further in familiar discourse with this young man, whom he envied. "The man at the gate said everybody was on board," he finally observed. "He said all the passes were taken up."

The operator shrugged indifferently. "I don't know anything about that," said he.

"I got a radio set of my own," Tom ventured. "It's just a small one—for boy scouts. It hasn't got much sending power."

"He used to be a boy scout," said the operator pleasantly. "That's where he first picked it up."

"The other operator?"

"Yup."

"I learned some myself," said Tom.

The operator did not seem inclined to talk more, and Tom went on along the deck where a few early risers were sauntering back and forth enjoying the fresh morning breeze. He noticed that life preservers were laid across the rail, loosely tied, and piled at intervals along the deck, loosely tied also.

He ate his breakfast with the deck stewards and their boys, and then went down into his own domains where, according to instructions, he took from a certain meathook a memorandum of what he was to bring up from below.

Descending the dark companionway, he turned on the electric light and stood puzzled for a moment, paper in hand. "That's just exactly like me," he said. "I got to admit it."

The fact was that despite his tour of initiation under the butcher's guidance he was puzzled to know which of the two doors opened into the room from which supplies for the voyage were to be drawn. At a hazard he opened one.

Sliding open one of the screen doors, he stooped and

lifted out a couple of cans from a lower shelf. As he did so he heard a familiar ticking sound which was pretty sure to accompany the stooping posture with him, and which always notified him that his big trusty nickel watch was dangling on its nickel chain.

But it was not dangling this time, and Tom paused in surprise, for the ticking continued quite audibly and apparently very close to him. He took out his watch and was surprised to find that its sound was quite distinct from another and slower ticking somewhere nearby. He looked about for a clock, but could see none.

Then, of a sudden, he lifted several more cans from the shelf and knelt down, holding his ear close to the space. From somewhere behind the cans came the steady tick, tick, tick, tick. . . .

For a moment he knelt there in surprise. Then hurriedly he lifted out can after can until there lay revealed upon the shelf a long, dark object. The ticking was louder now.

He touched the object gingerly and found that it was held fast in place by a wire, which ran from a screw in the shelf to another screw in the bulkhead above it, and was thus effectually prevented from moving with the rolling of the ship.

Something prompted Tom to step quickly through the passage to make sure that he had entered the right room. Then he discovered his mistake. The room he had entered was the storeroom from which no supplies were to be taken on the present trip. He turned back and knelt again.

Tick, tick, tick, tick. . . .

What did it mean? What should he do? His next impulse was to run upstairs and report what he had discovered. He did not dare touch the thing again.

Then he realized that something—something terrible—

might happen while he was gone. Something might happen in five minutes—the next minute—the next second! He watched the thing in a sort of fascination.

Tick, tick, tick—it went, on its steady grim journey toward. . . . Toward what?

Still Tom did not budge. As though hypnotized, he watched. Tick, tick, tick, tick, tick—it went; heedless, cheerful, like a clock on a mantelpiece. And still Tom Slade remained just where he was, stark still and trembling.

Then, of a sudden, Tom Slade, ship's boy, disappeared and there in his place was Tom Slade, scout. He cautiously removed the encircling wire, lifted the object out with both hands, finding it surprisingly heavy, and laid it carefully upon a table.

Tick, tick, tick, tick, tick—it went cheerfully along on its tragic errand.

It appeared to consist of a piece of ordinary stovepipe about twelve inches long. The face and works of an alarm clock, being of a slightly smaller circumference, had been placed within one end of the pipe, the face out, and the intervening space around this was packed with cotton waste. The other end of the pipe was closed with a kind of gummy cement.

Tom observed that the little alarm dial in the clock's face was set for nine o'clock, which afforded him infinite relief, for it was not yet seven.

With the greatest of care and hands trembling a little, he pulled out some of the cotton waste around the clock face, holding the dial steady with one hand, and found that nothing save this package was holding the clock in place. He joggled it very gently this way and that to make sure that it was not connected with anything behind. Then he lifted it out and put it on a shelf.

Tick, tick, tick, tick—it went just as before, as if not in the least disappointed that its tragic purpose had been thwarted.

There was no gold cross for this little act of Tom's and no "loud plaudits," as his chum Peewee would have said, but Tom Slade had saved a couple of hundred lives just the same.

It occurred to him now that pretty soon he would be expected upstairs. The hands of the clock pointed to a quarter of six, but Tom's own watch, which was as honest, plain, and reliable as he himself, said twelve minutes of seven. "That's funny," said he.

He peered into the space which the removal of the clock had left in the pipe's end. Four or five inches deep, it appeared to be sealed with the same gummy substance as at the other end. On the inside of the pipe was a rough-looking, yellowish area about two inches square, and from this two black, heavy cords ran to the cement wall.

Tom understood at once the mechanism of the horrible thing. The bell of the alarm clock had been removed and the clock so placed that at the fatal tick the striker would vibrate against this rough area, which was probably inflammable like a match end and which, on being ignited, would have ignited the fuse. Tom's imagination traced the hurrying little flames, racing along those cords, and he shuddered. His lip curled a little as he looked from the now harmless piece of junk to the impenitent clock, which was ticking merrily on. "Huh, I don't call that fighting," he said.

Tom's knowledge of war was confined to what he had learned at school. He knew about the battle of Bunker Hill and that ripping old fight, the battle of Lexington. These two encounters represented what he understood war to be. "That ain't fighting," he repeated.

Methodically, he went upstairs to his ultimate superior. "I got something to tell you, Mr. Cressey," he said hurriedly. "I made a mistake and went into the wrong room, and there's a bomb there. It was set for nine o'clock. I fixed it so's it can't go off."

"What?" ejaculated the steward.

"I fixed it so it can't go off," Tom repeated dully. "If I'd waited till I told you it might have gone off by mistake."

His manner was so entirely free from excitement that for a moment the steward could only stare at him.

"There ain't any danger now," said Tom.

The steward whistled to himself thoughtfully. "Go down there and wait till I come, and don't say anything about this to anybody," said he.

Tom went down, feeling quite important; he was being drawn head and shoulders into the war now. Once the thought occurred to him that perhaps he would be suspected of something.

In a few minutes the steward came down with the captain, and the first officer, and a man in civilian's clothes who carried a cigar in the corner of his mouth and who Tom thought must be of the secret service.

"Confirms your suspicions, eh?" said the captain to the man in plain clothes, after a gingerly inspection of the ominous piece of stovepipe.

"Hmmm," said the other man, "yes, no doubt of it. Wish I'd taken him up last trip when he sent that message. We'll have a job finding him now."

"I don't see how he could have got ashore since nine o'clock last night," said the first officer.

"Well, he did, anyway," said the secret-service man. "They're getting by every day and they will until we have martial law along the water front. You see this is where he

had to come through to his locker," he added, looking
about.

The captain gave a brief order to the first officer to have
the vessel searched at once for more bombs. The officer
hurried away and presently came back again. The secret-
service man was intently examining the floor, the jamb
around the door, and the casing of the porthole. The captain, too, scrutinized the place as if he hoped it might yield
some valuable information; and Tom, feeling very awkward, stood silently watching them.

"Here you are," said the secret-service man, indicating
a brown stain on the doorjamb.

The other three men stepped over to the spot, but Tom
did not dare to join them.

"There you are, Captain," said the secret-service man.
"See that finger mark? The skin lines aren't as clear, see?
That's from constant pressure. That's the finger he uses to
press his radio key."

"Hmm," said the captain.

"It was a lucky mistake this boy made," said the first
officer, glancing not unkindly at Tom.

"Mmmm," said the captain.

Tom did not know whether to take this for praise or not.
He stood, silent but very thoughtful. None of his four superiors took the trouble to acknowledge his act, nor even
to address him, and he had to piece together as best he
could, from their conversation, the reasons for their suspicions of the missing operator.

The secret-service man was very self-confident and very
convincing. Tom could not help envying and admiring him
from his obscure corner.

"I'll send a wire right away," said the captain, as the four
moved toward the door.

As they reached the door Tom spoke, his voice shaking a little, but in the slow, almost expressionless way which was characteristic of him. "If you'd wait a minute, I got something to say," he said.

"Yes, sir," said the first officer not unpleasantly. The captain paused impatiently. The secret-service man smiled a little.

"I heard this morning," said Tom, "that the other operator—the one that isn't here—that he used to be a boy scout. I'm a scout and so I know what kind of fellers scouts are. They ain't traitors or anything like that. If he was a scout then he wasn't a German, even if he might have had a German name, 'cause Germans stay by themselves and don't join in, kind of. . . ."

The captain made a move as if to go.

"But that ain't what I wanted to say," said Tom.

The captain paused. There was something about Tom's blunt, plain speech and slow manner which amused the first officer, and he listened with rather more patience than the others.

"There was a man tried to get off the ship last night," said Tom. "He. . . ."

"Oh, yes, that was Dr. Curry from Ohio," said the first officer with an indulgent laugh. "I hunted him up on the purser's list—he's all right. He flew off the handle because his baggage didn't come. He's all right, boy."

"The man that started the English scouts," said Tom, undaunted, "says if you want to find out if a person is foreign, you got to get him mad. Even if he talks good English, when he gets excited he'll say some words funny."

The captain turned upon his heel.

"But that ain't what I was going to say, either," said Tom dully. "Anybody that knows anything about radio work knows that operators have to have exactly the right time. That's the first thing they learn—that their watches have got to be exactly right—even to the second. I know 'cause I studied radio and I read the correspondence catalogues."

"Well?" encouraged the secret-service man.

But it was pretty hard to hurry Tom. "The person that put the bomb there," said he, "probably started it going and set it after he got it fixed on the shelf; and he most likely set it by his own watch. You can see that clock is over an hour slow. I was wondering how anybody's watch would be an hour slow, but if that Dr. Curry came from Ohio maybe he forgot to set his watch ahead in Cleveland. I know you have to do that when you come east 'cause I heard a man say so."

A dead silence prevailed, save for the subdued whistling of the secret-service man, as he scratched his head and eyed Tom sharply. "How old are you, anyway?" said he.

"Seventeen," said Tom. "A scout is a brother to every other scout—all over the world. Specially now when England and France are such close partners of ours, like. So I'm a brother to that radio operator, if he used to be a scout. Maybe I got no right to ask you to do anything, but maybe you'd find out if that man's watch is an hour slow. Maybe you'd be willing to do that before you send a wire."

The captain looked full at Tom, with a quizzical, shrewd look. He saw now, what he had not taken the trouble to notice before, a boy with a big mouth, a shock of rebellious hair, a ridiculously ill-fitting jacket, and a peaked cap set askew. Instinctively Tom pulled off his cap.

"What's your name?" said the captain.

"Tom Slade," he answered, nervously arranging his long arms in the troublesome, starched sleeves. "In the troop I used to belong to," he ventured to add, "they called me Sherlock Nobody Holmes, the fellers did, because I was interested in deduction and things like that."

For a moment the captain looked at him sternly. Then the secret-service man, still whistling with a strangely significant whistle, stepped over to Tom. "Put your cap on," said he, "frontways like that. Now come along with me and we'll see if Dr. Curry from Ohio can accommodate us with the time."

When that flippant youth Archibald Archer beheld Tom Slade hurrying along the promenade deck under the attentive convoy of one of Uncle Sam's sleuths, he was seized with a sudden fear that his protégé was being arrested as a spy.

The federal detective was small and agile, with a familiar, humorous way about him. He had a fashion of using his cigar as a sort of confidential companion, working it from one corner of his mouth to the other, and poking it up almost perpendicularly as he talked. Tom liked him at once, but he did not know whether or not to take literally all that he said.

"Conne is my name—Carleton Conne. Sounds like a detective in a story, don't it? My great-great-grandfather's mother-in-law on my sister's side was German. I'm trying to live it down."

"What?" said Tom.

Mr. Conne screwed his cigar over to the corner of his mouth and looked at Tom with a funny look. "We want to meet the doctor before he has a chance to change his watch," said Mr. Conne more soberly. "If he set that thing a little after nine last night (and he couldn't have set it before) he was probably too busy thinking of getting off the ship to think of much else. He ought to be just coming out of his stateroom by now. We must see him before he sees a clock. You get me?"

"Yes, sir," said Tom, a little anxious, "but I might be wrong after all."

"Maybe," said Mr. Conne. "There are three things we will have to judge by. There's his trying to get off the ship last night, and there's the question of how his watch stands, and there's the question of how he acts when we talk with him—see?"

"Yes, sir."

"Since you're a detective, remember this," Mr. Conne added good-humoredly, "it's part of the *A B C* of the business. Three middle-sized clues are better than one big one —if they hang together. Six little ones aren't as good as three middle-sized ones, because sometimes they seem to hang together when they don't really—see?"

"Yes, sir."

"Where'd you ever get your eyes and ears, anyway?" said Mr. Conne abruptly.

"You learn to observe when you're a scout," said Tom.

Here and there little groups of passengers stood chatting as they waited for breakfast. Among them were a few men in khaki, whom Tom understood to be army surgeons and engineers—the forerunners of the legions who would come across later.

"Which would you rather be?" queried Mr. Conne. "A detective or a radio operator?"

"I'd rather be a regular soldier," said Tom, "I made up my mind to it. I'm only waiting till I'm eighteen."

Mr. Conne gave him a shrewd sidewise glance, his cigar pointing upward like a piece of field artillery. "Well, I guess if you've got your mind made up you'll do it," said he.

"But I hope I can work on this ship when she's a regular transport and keep working on her till I'm eighteen."

"You haven't answered my question yet."

"I don't know which I'd rather be," said Tom.

"Hmmm," said Mr. Conne.

"What do you suppose became of the other operator?" Tom asked, a little anxiously.

"I don't know," said Mr. Conne. "We'll have to find someone who does know," he added significantly, and Tom wondered what he meant.

"Do you think he's guilty of anything?" he asked.

"Don't know. You've knocked my theories all endways, young fellow," Mr. Conne said pleasantly, and then added, smiling, "you say he was a scout; I'm getting to have a pretty good opinion of scouts."

"But those fingerprints. . . ."

"Were his," concluded Mr. Conne.

Tom was greatly puzzled, but he said nothing. Soon Dr. Curry appeared. He was pacing up and down the deck and paused at the rail as they neared, so that they were able to get a good look at him. He was tall and thin, with a black mustache and a very aristocratic hooked nose. Perhaps there was the merest suggestion of the foreigner about him, but nothing in particular to suggest the German.

Mr. Conne sauntered up to him with a friendly and familiar air, though Tom was trembling all over. "Excuse me, would you oblige me with the time?" Mr. Conne said, pleasantly.

The stranger wheeled about suddenly with a very pronounced military air and looked at his questioner. "The time? Yes, sir," he said with brisk formality and taking out his watch. "It is just half past six."

Mr. Conne drew out his own watch and looked at it for a moment as if perplexed. "Then one of us is about an hour out of the way," he said sociably, while Tom stood by in anxious suspense. "According to the alarm down in the storeroom I guess you're right," he added.

"What?" said the passenger, disconcerted.

"According to the time bomb down below," repeated Mr. Conne, still sociably, but with a keen, searching look. "What's the matter? Suffering from nerves, Doctor?"

The sudden thrust, enveloped in Mr. Conne's easy manner, had indeed taken the doctor almost off his feet. "I do not understand you, sir," he said, with forbidding dignity and trying to regain his poise.

"Well, then, I'll explain," said Mr. Conne. "You forgot to set your watch when you left Cleveland, Doc, and there won't be any explosion down below at nine o'clock, and there won't be any at all, so don't worry."

He worked his cigar over into the corner of his mouth and looked up at his victim in a tantalizing manner, waiting. And he was not disappointed, for in the angry tirade which the passenger uttered it became very apparent that he was a foreigner. Mr. Conne seemed quietly amused.

"Doc," said he sociably, almost confidentially, "I believe if it hadn't been for this youngster here, you'd have gotten away with it. It's too bad about your watch being slow— German reservists and ex-army officers ought to remember that this is a wide country. When you're coming across Uncle Sam's back yard to blow up ships, it's customary to put your watch an hour ahead in Cleveland, Doc. Where's all your German efficiency? Here's a wide-awake young American youngster got you beaten to a standstill. . . ."

"This is abominable!" roared the man.

"Say that again, Doc," said Mr. Conne with a laugh. "I like the way you say it when you're mad. So that's why you didn't get off the ship in time last night, eh?" he added with a touch of severity. "Watch slow! Bah! You're a bungler, Doc! Here's an American boy, never studied the German spy system, and by jingoes, he's tripped you up —and saved a dozen ships and half-a-dozen munition factories, for all I know. German efficiency—bah! The boy scouts have got you nailed to the mast!"

Then, suddenly, the detective became serious. "You'll have to show me your passport, sir," he said, "and any other papers you have. Then I'm going to lock you up."

The next morning Tom met Mr. Conne.

"Well, I see the captain beat me to it," said he. "I was thinking of working you into the secret service, but never mind, there's time enough. You go ahead and make good as assistant to the radio operator."

"Maybe I won't satisfy them. Sometimes I make mistakes," said Tom. "I made a mistake when I went into the wrong storeroom, if it comes to that. They always called me bullhead, the fellers in the troop did."

Mr. Conne cocked his head sideways, screwed his cigar over to the extreme corner of his mouth and looked at Tom with a humorous scrutiny. "Did they?" said he. "All right, Tommy. Uncle Sam and I mean to keep our eyes on you, just the same."

On Leave

BY STUART CLOETE

He was nearly there now. Henri Baptiste, of the 33rd
Regiment of Chasseurs, looked about him. It was the same,
but different. The war, of course. It was the war that made
a difference, but he was nearly there. Nearly home. He
looked at the big poplars that lined the road. One of them
was cut off like a match—splintered. Most of the trees
were scarred, but this was the first broken one. It had
been a business getting this leave. When they asked where
he wanted to go, he had told them.

"Berie le Grand," he had said.

"But that is on the front. That is in English lines. You can't go there."

"It is my home," he said. "It is the only place for me to go. I am alone."

"Is your house there?" the commandant had asked.

"The house is destroyed, *mon commandant*," he had said. "But my home is there—my land."

They had let him go. And everyone had been very kind. The colonel had given him a letter. The general of brigade, the general of division had given him letters. The interpreter from headquarters had given him a letter in English for the English and Americans he would meet. Then he had gone, in full marching order, by train to the English railhead. From there he had marched, a French soldier in horizon blue marching through a France held by English and Americans. That was funny, was it not? Very funny, if it had not been sad. They had been good to him, those others along the road. He had shown his papers to everyone; he had saluted countless officers in cars, on horseback, on foot. He had stood on the side of the road, at attention, with his arms sloped, as their columns passed. At night he had slept among them and they had fed him.

Yes, everyone had been good to him. They had given him lifts on their trucks, on their limbers and wagons. A general had stopped his car to ask him what he was doing, and he had shown him his letters. A lieutenant had let him march with his platoon, because, as everyone knows, it is easier to march with others than to walk alone. He had marched at the head of the platoon with the officer, a young boy who could talk a little French. Those men were his comrades. They were over here fighting for France. He shifted his rifle from his left shoulder to his right. That was a funny thing, too—how your rifle got heavier as the hours passed. And he was tired. When he had been young,

on his service, how they had marched—sixty kilometers a
day sometimes. But he was no longer so young. From the
next hill he would be able to see the church tower of Mir-
baux. He walked faster. Now he should see it. . . . No,
not yet.

He increased his pace. He was at the top of the hill.
Perhaps he was on the wrong road. But that was impossible. There was the valley with the stream running through
it, and the bridge. There were trout under that bridge. He
had caught them there as a boy. Fat trout that lay in the
shadowy ripples facing upstream, with just their tails moving. He laid his rifle on the ground and raised both hands
to shade his eyes. The steeple should have come out of the
woods beyond the stream. The village was hidden behind
it. But the wood did not look quite the same.

He thought of the poplar tree. . . . That was it—the
war. It was the war. The steeple was gone. Strange that
you were used to all that in your own sector, but it was
hard to think of it at home. But why should the church at
home not go as much as any other? Did it matter to anyone
that he had made his first Communion and had been married in it? After all, his house was gone too. He had been
told that, but it was hard to visualize it. You could visualize things that were there, but it was hard to visualize the
removal of things, like a wood, or a church, or your own
house. He rubbed the front of his thighs. He saw a broken
limber by the side of the road with a dead horse near it.
He was not far now. They had said, "You'll come to the
communication trench soon after you pass the limber and
dead horse." This road led to his house. *That is, where my
house was,* he thought, *but it was in view of the enemy.*

He began to look for the opening of the trench; the road
was sunken here, with high grass banks. There were things
lying about—leaking water tins, some old equipment, a

broken rifle. This must be where the rations were brought by the regimental transport. Battalion headquarters was near the road, they said. He stopped and put down his rifle. He must tidy himself. He could not appear at a strange headquarters like this.

He took off his pack. He brushed his coat with his hand. He wiped his rifle and the hilt of his bayonet with his handkerchief. Dust was on everything. He squared his shoulders to loosen them. It was good to be without the pack for a moment. He looked at it as it lay on the grass. He knelt down and rearranged the roll of his coat, fastened the lid of his canteen tighter. Then he put on his pack, tightened his belt, and went on.

There was another dead horse. It was funny that a dead horse smelled different from a dead mule. A mule was sweeter, more sickly. Some men said English and French dead smelled different from the Germans. He had never noticed it himself. As far as he could see, one dead man smelled like another. It all depended on the weather and how long they had been dead. It depended, too, on the soil; some soil preserved bodies wonderfully. A clay soil, for instance. That must be because it was close-grained and excluded the air. They said it was diet that made one race smell different from another. It might be so. Men even smelled different when they were alive. The Chinese said we smelled terrible, but he had liked Indochina all the same; Saigon was a wonderful place.

There it was—Canal Street—painted very neatly in black on a white board. Under it, someone had written, "Piccadilly, a hundred and three miles." Piccadilly was like the Rue de la Paix, or the Place de la Concorde. A good sense of humor they had. Yes, it was funny. He stopped to look back down the road. Pure white, it shone in the sun, so that you had to half close your eyes to see it.

The dead horse was a big black patch on the white. It was swollen as if it had drowned. Its legs stood up in the air. No doubt, soon someone would stick a bayonet in its belly and let out the gas; then it would shrivel up.

His house was two kilometers from here. "Piccadilly, a hundred and three miles." A kilometer was five eighths of an English mile. There were chalk walls on each side of him. Above him, a frill against the sky, was the grass. There were flowers hanging over the edge of the trench—red poppies, blue cornflowers, marguerites, clover, and here and there a wild yellow snapdragon. A lark sang in the air. It was high summer. That was why the grass was so long and the larks sang. Harvest time.

The trench took a sweeping turn. That was so that the stretchers could be carried down easily. No sharp turns in a communication trench. He heard voices. Another minute. . . .

"Here, what's this! It's a Frenchy . . . ! What are you doing here?"

"He's in marching order."

It was the headquarters. There was a dugout, with the signalers sitting on the steps, telephone in hand. There were orderlies waiting. A group of stretcher-bearers stood together, their stretchers upright against the side of the trench. They all came toward him. He presented his letter to a sergeant who had a number of ribbons on his chest. He read it slowly and pushed his helmet back over his ears.

"What is it?" someone said. "What's he doing here?"

"This is his home," the sergeant said. "He wants to spend his leave at home. . . . Here," he said, "you must come to the colonel." He took him by the arm.

"Lives here, does he?" someone asked. "Fine place to live, I must say."

There was more talk. Cigarettes were pushed into his hand—a packet. He took them and put them into his pocket.

The sergeant was shouting into a dugout. "Sergeant Major!" he shouted. "Sergeant Major, here's a Frenchman!"

The sergeant major came out. A big, red-faced man with two rows of ribbons.

"Read this," the sergeant said. He read it.

"Come with me," the sergeant major said. He followed the wide trench back into a cut that led into an old quarry. He suddenly remembered it. There was a cave here. He had played in the cave with the others when he was a boy. That was funny, too—his cave a British battalion headquarters.

There were the officers. They were eating round a table. They were very young—almost boys.

"What's this, Sergeant Major?" one of them said.

Henri looked at his shoulder straps—a crown and a star —a lieutenant colonel. Just about the age of his eldest son. He must not think of his sons. It was no use thinking of the dead. Three boys dead.

The sergeant major gave the colonel his letter. Perhaps the colonel could read French. Holding his rifle between his knees, he felt for his other letters—the one from the generals of division and brigade, his colonel's letter. They all said much the same thing:

> Private Henri Baptiste requests permission to visit his home, which is situated in the British line. General Devaux would consider it a kindness if the British officer in command of that section of the line would accord Private Henri Baptiste this favor. Private Henri Baptiste is a soldier of the first class, twice decorated for gallantry in the field. His three sons

have died fighting for France, and his wife and daughter are believed held by the enemy, being overtaken as they sought refuge from their home.

He found them, straightened up, and put them on the table beside the colonel. Then he stood at attention and waited. His eyes were fixed on the blue sky at the mouth of the cave. In a minute he would know. In a minute they would tell him if he could go on. He had come so far, but orders were orders. If they said "No," then he must march back. In a minute he would know. He looked at the sky. He did not dare look at the young colonel's face. It reminded him of Jerome—Sergeant Jerome Baptiste. . . . "We regret to inform you that your son, Sergeant Jerome Baptiste, was killed in action . . . heroic . . . performance of his duty . . . decorated . . . his comrades—"

He watched a lark falling—perhaps it had a nest. Birds did not mind war. Especially the larks. Gunfire seemed to excite them, to make them sing. It disturbed them and sent them up, singing, into the air. The colonel had his other letters. He had picked them up. Henri watched him out of the corner of his eye.

He was talking. He said, "He's on leave. His home is our line."

"Leave?" another officer said. "My God, on leave here!"

The colonel was speaking to him now. "You can go," he said. He looked at the colonel's chest. He did not want to see his face. Two ribbons, one blue and red, one purple and white. Those were medal ribbons for bravery. "Go with the sergeant major," the colonel said in French. "He will give you a guide."

"Thank you, *mon colonel*. And I can remain?" It was that that mattered. He must remain.

"As long as you like," the colonel said.

"Thank you, *mon colonel.*"

"Come," the sergeant major said.

He saluted, and turned about.

"Orderly!" the sergeant major shouted. "Orderly!"

A man came running.

"Take this man up to A Company. He can go where he likes, the colonel said."

He saluted again. Everyone was very kind. He followed the orderly up the trench. When they had gone a few yards, the orderly stopped.

"Cigarette?" he said.

"Thank you." Perhaps he would like some wine. He undid his water bottle.

"*Vin,*" the orderly said, putting out his hand. "*Bon vin.*" He laughed.

They went on. He was almost home. He had thought about this moment for months. The communication trench wound through the chalk. There were more flowers, more larks sang. A partridge having a dust bath on the parapet flew away on whirring wings. They came to an S-shaped trench block and a machine-gun post, the junction of another trench running at right angles. A support trench, no doubt. Company headquarters would be here. They turned down it. Sentries looked through periscopes in every bay, men lay asleep on the fire step and in little holes they had carved out of the chalk. Two men stripped to the waist were going through the seams of their gray shirts for lice. Everything was the same as in the French line, but different—just enough different to make it interesting, while one still felt at home.

There were signalers sitting in the mouth of a deep dugout. Signalers always seemed to sit on the steps. A stretcher-bearer was lying asleep in his stretcher. His helmet was beside him. He had a red handkerchief over his eyes. There was a smell of chloride of lime. Some must have been thrown down here, but you could not see it on the chalk. His guide shouted. He was handed over to another sergeant, received by another young officer. Men crowded round him, giving him more cigarettes, rum and water, tea, bully beef. Everyone was very kind. The officer pointed to the signalers' dugout. Henri took off his pack and hung it on some pegs driven into the wall. He sat on the fire step and began to smoke. Well, here he was. He was back. He must rest, reorganize himself, and then make a little tour.

"Have a peep," the sentry said. He pushed the periscope toward him.

"Thank you." Now was the moment. *Courage,* he said to himself. *Courage.* He braced his shoulders. He was looking out into no man's land. This was what he had come to see. He searched for landmarks. He could just see the German wire. It was about two hundred meters away. There was an old ditch, but that didn't say anything to him. There were some tree stumps—biggish trees they must have been. He tried to recall any big trees near his house. There had been none. Yes, there had. Willows, pollarded, so that one did not think of them as big, on Vasseur's place. The ditch, then; that was Vasseur's ditch. It carried floodwater from between their gardens. His house must be to the right, over there. He turned the mirror a little. Over there there was nothing. If only he could have looked over the top with glasses. He knew he was staring at his house and could not see it. Then he saw it. There was a low heap of brick rubble. He recognized it by the line of young fruit trees he had planted along the back. Pears, they were, and all seemed to have remained, but they had grown from below the graft. They needed pruning badly. The sentry came and peered into the periscope. He looked up and smiled.

"Boche," he said, "rat-tat-tat." He made the movement of traversing a gun. "Cave," he said. "Boche in cave." Then he took the periscope back.

So there was a machine-gun post in his cellar. They had been proud of their cellar; everything kept so cool and sweet in it—milk, butter, potatoes, strings of onions. It was dry, too; nothing ever went moldy. He lit another cigarette. The first pause was over. He had seen what he had come to see. They had told him the truth. His house was destroyed. The English line ran through the bottom of his garden. Two years ago he had had potatoes there, on Vasseur's boundary.

There were some bombs on the parapet beside him. He picked one up.

"Here, don't muck them about," the sentry said.

They did not want him to touch them. It was his business; he was a grenadier. *"Grenadier,"* he said, pointing to himself. *"Expliquez."*

"Explain, hey? Well, it's this way." The soldier took the bomb in his hand, pretended to pull out the pin, and made the gesture of throwing. Then he unscrewed the aluminum base and showed him the inside.

He nodded; it was simple enough. He went through the motions in his mind: pull out the pin, throw; when you let go, the handle flew off and the striker hit the fulminate of mercury, setting off the charge. He nodded his head. An officer passed down the trench. The officer on duty.

Henri Baptiste saluted. The officer stopped. Henri pointed to the bombs, and made a motion of throwing, then he held up one finger. *"Pour essayer,"* he said.

"What do you want?" the officer asked. "To throw

one . . . ? Does he understand them, White?" He had turned to the sentry.

"I've explained them, sir," the soldier said.

The officer nodded his head. "Just one," he said, and held up his finger.

They were good, these people—very hospitable and friendly. There seemed to be nothing they would not do to make him happy. He took a bomb. It felt good in his hand. He looked behind him. There was plenty of room. The trench was wide—too wide really—but good to throw from. He put his finger in the ring that held the pin. It came out easily. The bomb was dangerous now. It was in his right hand. He bent his right shoulder, dropping it a little. He balanced himself on his feet, his left foot raised, his left hand up. Again he balanced his body, bent right over; his left hand was against the sky, his right hand came up as his left arm and foot came down. The bomb left his hand. He saw it going up and up. It was a good throw. It began to fall. There was a pause, an explosion.

"Thank you, *mon lieutenant*," he said.

The officer was smiling. "You are a good bomber," he said.

"Good. *Oui, grenadier*," he said.

They were good, these people. They let him do everything. There was just one thing more. He stood to attention.

"*Ce soir*," he said. "Bomb." Then he pointed toward the wire and to himself. Would they let him go? Would they give him some bombs and let him go? He would go by himself. It would interfere with no one. He had thought of it so long.

"Patrol," the officer said. So he understood. "You want to go out tonight—*ce soir?*"

"*Oui, mon lieutenant.*" Would they let him go?

The lieutenant began to laugh. Henri knew what he was laughing at. He thought it was a funny way for a man to spend his leave. He thought, why does he not go to Paris and have a good time with wine and the girls? There was always wine and the girls for soldiers, even if they had no money. He did not understand that he was spending his leave at home. That the trench they were standing in was in his garden; that those pear trees that needed pruning were his. He did not understand. How could he understand, when one could hardly understand, oneself?

"Yes, you can go," the officer said.

At last it was night. He had everything. Bombs; a revolver lent him, with the officer's permission, by one of the Lewis-gun section; food that they did not know about; and a water bottle full of weak rum and water, and some little arrangements of his own—a parcel that he had carried in his pack. His rifle and equipment he left behind him. You wanted freedom. Several men had offered to go with him. The officer had offered a strong patrol; there had been several efforts to get that post, but all had failed. He refused everything with thanks. They were very kind, too kind, but it was best that he go alone. He knew the country. He nearly laughed as he said that. Yes, he knew it. He had dug it over each year by hand.

What was his plan?

He did not know. The plan would come when he was out there. But when they heard his bombs, would they support him with machine-gun fire?

Word was passed down the line that the Frenchman was going out. They were to be ready to cover him and let him in. A man was never certain to come back into the line at the same place as he left it. A man was never certain to come back.

The night was very quiet. There was some distant shelling, a few flares went up, the officer on duty fired a Very light from his pistol. On the left, a mile or so away, there were German lights—two green balls and a red, then a golden shower. Signals. Some explosions of trench mortars —big ones, flying pigs—and a burst of artillery fire—three or four salvos. Then silence again. The men, except for the sentries, were half-asleep in the trench; their rifles, with bayonets fixed, beside them. It was no hardship sleeping out on such a night. The officer came back from his rounds. He lit a cigarette. The cupped match lit up his face. A shell, sounding like a train, came toward them.

Henri heard the explosion of the gun, then the shell, getting nearer and nearer. It would be annoying to be wounded now. It seemed to take minutes coming. It was like a train, getting louder and louder. It struck short— about twenty yards away. A big one—five-nine. A shower of earth scattered over him. The explosion threw everything into sharp light and shade—the trench, the men cowering. Someone cried out. There was a shout of "Stretcher-bearers!" The officer ran toward the boy who had been hit. Henri waited for more. There were no more. It was just a single shell.

He looked at the moon. It was just right. Just as he had calculated it. There were a few clouds. He waited for a cloud to cover the moon and put his hand onto the peg he had driven into the parapet. The world was suddenly enlarged. It seemed enormous. He pulled himself right up, stood erect to make certain of his direction, and dropped to his knees. With his hands he began to feel for the wire; there was a gap here. He lay down and looked at the wire, black against the sky. A barb caught at his sleeve. He disengaged himself. He was past the wire. He was in the open. A German flare went up. He flattened himself and waited for the light to die down. He did not look up—

that was how you got seen. Not that he would be seen, since he had blackened his face and hands with burnt cork and oil. There were the stars that gave him his line. That was the best of being a country man—you knew the stars. He crawled on. He went very slowly. There was no hurry. The sweat poured off him. The bombs were heavy and interfered with his movement. It could not be far now. He listened. He could hear them talking. He wished he understood German. There would be four men there, or six at most. The gun crew and some bombers.

Those German bombs were nothing unless they hit you or were very near. There was no danger. The gun began to fire, traversing the front; bullets passed just over his head. He watched the fire sputtering from the muzzle as it swung round. The burst stopped. They had just fired off half a belt on the chance of hitting someone.

He crawled on. The plan was working. It depended now on one thing. Had they found the drain he had dug near the cellar? He had never really completed it. It had not been necessary; the cellar had proved so dry. Nothing ever went moldy in it, and few people could say that of their cellars. Of course, the Germans would be wired in, but there must be a way. . . . He was very close now and could hear them moving about. A wiring party was now working in front of their line. That accounted for the fact that there had been only one burst of fire and that they had sent up no more lights. The hole should be here. Just here somewhere. He began to feel about. He did not want to fall into it. There it was. He dropped into it carefully and pulled the long grass over his head. It was funny to be sitting in a drain you had dug. He had meant to fill it up with loose stones.

He settled down. It was very snug here, and safe as being at home. It almost made one laugh. He had a mouthful of rum and water and ate a biscuit and some bully beef. Then he dozed. There was plenty of time. The cold of the dawn woke him. They were talking loud now, and laughing. It was the relief. He heard the new men settling in and others going out. They went over the top. He counted them. Four only, there were, and no trench leading to their line. He had been afraid of a sap. It would have made things harder. The cut through the wire that they used was quite near him. Everything was going splendidly. Everything was in his favor.

His hand went to his back—the fishing rod was safe—into his pocket—the bomb and the fuse were there. That was a fine bomb he had made. Perhaps he should not have carried it in his equipment when he traveled, but he had been careful. Bombs had become his business. He slept very well with a bag of bombs as a pillow. The sun rose higher. A covey of partridges whirred over him and landed somewhere near. A hare pushed the grass aside as it went past. Animals and birds had lost all fear of man. He saw a big rat, blotched and mangy. They got like that, living on bodies. Three magpies flew overhead, chattering. That was a lucky sign. It was getting hotter. The hotter the better. The sun was high now. The moment approached. The Boches were moving about; he could hear them talking again, and the rattle of their canteens. He could smell the smoke of their cigars. It was the devil not being able to smoke. How long did it take to smoke a cigar? Fifteen minutes? He looked at his watch. Better allow thirty. It was very hot, very quiet.

Now it was time. From his back he took a little bundle of short lengths of bamboo—his friend, Lamarche, had made them for him from a fishing rod cut into short sections. On the first section there was a ring. He laid the rods down carefully in a line, side by side. There must be no error. From his pocket he took his bomb and twenty feet of fuse. He fitted the fuse into the detonator, put it between his teeth and clinched it. Then he tied the bomb to the ring and pushed it down the drain. The next section was fitted to it, and the next. The fuse was uncoiling like a snake.

Provided they had not filled in the bottom of the cellar —and why should they?—it would be all right. That is, if none of them noticed it coming. The last section now. A good thing he knew the exact distance—three meters exactly. He lit the fuse and crawled into the long grass. There would be a kickback from the bomb, but most of it would go off into the cellar. Were his calculations right? Were they fully fed and asleep in the sun. He had a Mills bomb in each hand. The safety pins were out. As soon as he heard the explosion, he would lob them in. Three meters—you did not have to be a bomber to do that; just drop them in underarm.

The explosion came. There were shouts of pain. He let his bombs go. . . . Right . . . left. They exploded. His revolver was in his hand, cocked. No signs from the German lines. The explosions must have been regarded as normal, and the cries unheard. He had plenty of time. He was trembling now. His teeth chattered. He crawled forward, parting the grass with his pistol. He came to the little path they used on relief. He crawled down it and peered into the cellar. Four men dead, one nearly blown to pieces. Those English bombs were beautiful. He dropped in.

A lark was singing. It was hotter than ever. Abandoning his bombs, except two—one in each trouser pocket—he picked up the gun. He could carry it. He got it onto the little path. He got it into the long grass, crawling a yard, dragging the gun and crawling again. How far was it? Two hundred meters that had stretched suddenly to ten kilometers. He must go on. The English would be pleased. The gun was a nice return for their hospitality.

His hands were bleeding; he must go on.

The wire at last. He called out. Someone answered. There were shouts, "The Frenchman's in!" They knew where he was. He was back, but he could go no farther. He saw big spots moving in front of his eyes—white ones, marbled with black edges that ran into each other. He was back; they were dead. The gun. . . . He felt someone get hold of him. They were dragging him in. Now he could rest. There were just the trees to prune, but that would be easy, now that the English held his house. Tomorrow night, the night after. . . . There was time. He had a month's leave of absence. What was it they said? "The gun?" Yes, he had the gun. Four Boches dead. "He's got the gun! The Frenchy's got the gun! Four Jerries dead!"

The march back was the same as the march forward had been. The road was the same, everything was the same. Only the direction was different. He had the same lifts along the road, slept in the same places, spoke to some of the same men. He had come out of the communication trench and turned right by the dead horse in the road; he passed the other dead horse and the broken limber. He had stopped at the top of the hill to look at the wood where the church had been and the valley and the trout stream. After that, he had gone on, marching, halting, resting on the side of the road with his head on his pack.

The English general had offered to send him back by car. He had refused the offer. He wanted to march and to think as he marched. Left . . . right . . . left . . . right. His heavy boots, hitting the road, helped him to think. There was a rhythm in marching that did something to your head. It was good to march. And besides, he was nervous of automobiles; not afraid, just nervous. He had never been in one, but that was not a thing to tell an English general.

How good they were. How kind. After he had come back with the gun, the general had come up to inspect the line. He had asked him if there was anything he wanted, anything he could do for him. He had said that he would be recommended for a decoration—the English medal for distinguished conduct—but was there nothing. . . . It would be a pleasure.

There had been something. Would the general please find out if his wife and daughter were alive? He had written down their names in the general's notebook. He understood that there were ways of finding out through the Red Cross in Switzerland and Holland. Most officers knew about their families in the German lines, but for a simple soldier it was not so easy. Naturally, there were so many simple soldiers—hundreds of thousands of them with relations and homes in German hands. But the general had said he would see to it; that in a few weeks, a couple of months at most, he would have news.

There was Doullens. How often he had been here. At the *Three Loving Sisters* he had eggs, and fried potatoes, and meat, and cheese, and wine, and coffee with brandy. Everyone was so kind. The officers, the men, even the red-caps, the military police, were kind. They all seemed to know about him. The Frenchman who had taken a German machine gun at Ayette and brought it back to the Durham lines. They thought a lot of it.

Well, it was something, but the gun had been in his cellar. That annoyed a man. That sent a man mad. No, he must not think like that. He must hold himself in. If they were alive, they would need him after. He thought of what he would do. How he would rebuild. He thought of his pear trees. They were pruned and the suckers removed. Only three were dead. That was remarkable, when you came to think of it—only three out of twenty.

The railway transport officer gave him his papers. Now he was off. It was over. In two days he would be back with his regiment. It would be good to see his friends again. But he had been happy with the English. They had been good to him, his English comrades—food, cigarettes, rum, everything—but he had missed his wine. They had shown him pictures of their wives and girls, of their babies. They had talked to him and shared everything with him.

Well, it was over. He got out and walked beside the train to pick some flowers. He had a great weakness for flowers. He ate his rations; he slept, and at last, looking out, he saw blue instead of khaki. He was with his people again. Only a few more hours and he would be back.

They passed quickly. Almost before he knew it, he was there. Some of the transport of division was at the railhead. He got a lift on a wagon. . . . Yes, he had been on leave. He had been home. . . . Yes, he had enjoyed it. He had had a wonderful time. His pack was filled with cigarettes, with tobacco, with a bottle of rum, a pipe. They had loaded him with gifts. And in his pocket was a letter from the English general to his general. Funny to have so many letters from generals. They were going to decorate him. He might be sent for to England, to London, they said. That would mean going in a boat. He was not sure about that. It might be best to refuse the decoration, but that would be an insult to his friends.

He thought of his English friends again, of their good-bys. The English sergeant had looked funny when he kissed him, but what else could one do? He loved him. He loved them all. He had kissed them all, except the young officer. He had saluted him, and the officer had taken him

by the hand. There had been tears in that boy's eyes.
There had been tears in his own. It was a great moment.
Then he had marched away from them all, with his rifle at
the trail, his canteen rattling on the top of his pack. He got
off the wagon. He was marching again. Another hour and
he would be there.

"Private Henri Baptiste reporting for duty," he said.

"Henri Baptiste, so you're back."

"I am back, *mon capitaine*."

"It went well?"

"It was all right, *mon capitaine*. Everyone was **very**
kind. I thank you."

"And your home?"

"In the English lines, *mon capitaine*."

"And where did you go when you had seen it?"

"I stayed, *mon capitaine*. I spent my leave in my home."

He saluted and turned about. News in two months at
most, the English general said. They were strong women,
and might easily be alive.

The Net Result

BY RALPH D. PAINE

"This here war is no place for a nervous man," casually remarked a large, melancholy bluejacket, who tottered under the weight of another sandbag.

"You said something. There's times when you're almost lucid," replied a runt of a boatswain's mate as he halted to shift his own burden.

They trudged onward to join their comrades, who carried planks and rusted plates of sheet iron as well as sandbags, while other squads sweated with shovel and mattock. The winter rain pelted and drenched them, whipped by a gale which lashed the shallow harbor of Dunkirk into muddy froth and compelled the brave little trawlers to forsake their task of mine sweeping and come rolling in for shelter. Between the basins where the vessels were moored against the walls of masonry, there was a small area of wharfage now tenanted by several shacks and barracks of rough lumber above which snapped a frayed ensign, the Stars and Stripes.

What chiefly interested the toiling draft of a hundred and fifty men from the American Navy was the completion of a bomb-proof refuge spacious enough to contain all hands. Just why the higher powers should have elected to establish a seaplane base in this forlorn and battered port of the French coast was beyond their understanding, but they felt a lively regard for the safety of their own skins, and therefore they were digging themselves in with the most earnest zeal. The lieutenant in command, spattered with mud from his rubber boots to the disreputable blouse, showed them how to cover the roof with four feet of sand and a final layer of boiler plate. He was an energetic young man, incurably cheerful, who seemed not in the least dismayed at the prospect of being bombed from the air almost every night.

A few nights after the shelter was completed, Lieutenant Chuck Bevans, his two ensigns, and his hundred and fifty bluejackets tumbled out when the sirens shrieked and scrambled into their cavern while the Boche planes droned overhead and let fall the wicked projectiles that exploded with terrifying concussions and great flashes of flame. Although aimed at the docks and the shipping, most of them went wide of the mark, smashing through dwelling houses or tearing holes in the pavement. A British cargo steamer was demolished no more than a hundred yards from the American naval base, and another bomb glanced from the sloping roof of the dugout.

There followed a week of clear weather with light winds,

and the enemy squadrons visited Dunkirk every night, unloading their infernal freightage with more enthusiasm than accuracy, but managing to slay many women and children in the town, blowing the stern off an anchored French destroyer, and making life most unhappy for the Yankee sailormen. One barracks building was splintered, and a chasm of a hole marked the site of the shack in which the lieutenant had lived the simple life. The loss of sleep was trying to the nerves. A man couldn't keep it up indefinitely—working hard all day and crowding into a filthy dugout after dark while the cursed tumult sounded as though the world was tumbling about his ears.

The two ensigns were impatient and displayed irritation. This preliminary program was stupid. The lieutenant was awaiting the arrival of additional aviators before beginning the regular patrol against the German submarines in the Channel. Meanwhile the routine comprised a great deal of drudgery and no retaliation. The unhappy brace of ensigns were permitted to undertake practice flights in a French seaplane by way of learning how to rise from the narrow lane of water between the docks, a hazardous performance which risked an unholy crash at every attempt. Enviously they watched the British naval airmen soar far out to sea in their little fighting machines or heard their yarns of U-boats detected and reported to the surface fleets of destroyers, trawlers, and drifters, which hastened to administer the deadly depth bomb in a warfare that gave no quarter.

"What do you say to suggesting it to Bevans?" said Ensign Robert Carnahan, hopefully addressing his partner. "It isn't as if we were green at the game. We had a solid year's training at home before we came to France, and I'll bet we can fly with any of these birds on patrol duty."

"He says he needs us ashore," was the gloomy reply,

"and he is none too keen about drowning us until he gets more help."

"But if we stick around this dump much longer, Bob, we'll never get action. The old Boche mighty near scuppered the outfit last night. Man, he fairly ringed us with bombs. He is liable to score a touchdown before we beat it into the dugout one of these fine evenings, and there won't be enough left of two promising young aviators to make a funeral. I am certainly fed up with Dunkirk."

"You're on, Al. We'll put it up to Bevans at supper. One little war flight and we promise to be good."

The weary lieutenant, who was a regular navy man, inured to thankless duties and rigid discipline, knew what was in the minds of these boyish reserve ensigns. To them the war was a sporting adventure. Bob Carnahan had been a football player of campus renown, and Al Chew had pitched illustriously for the nine of another university. All they yearned for now was an opportunity to prove themselves, to gain a brief and glorious respite from the routine of the day's work. Lieutenant Chuck Bevans, condemned to serve as a head carpenter, mechanic, and taskmaster, smiled tolerantly as he observed the ensigns nudge each other and whisper at the supper table.

"How did the old boat tune up today?" he inquired.

"Smooth as a Swiss watch," Carnahan eagerly assured him. "Plenty of pep, and a child could have handled her."

"Some ship," put in Ensign Chew. "She did ninety knots and was just jogging."

"What about machine-gun practice?" pursued the lieutenant.

"We are really good, sir," modestly answered Bob Carnahan. "If we are ever lucky enough to meet a German plane, I'll bet I can shoot the eyebrows off the Fritzies."

"I presume you are a hundred per cent plus at bombing submarines," amiably observed their commander.

"Well, we let go four dummies today," came from Ensign Alfred Chew, "and every one of them would have put a hole through your hat."

"You *are* a couple of shrinking violets. It's all wasted, though, for I made up my mind to. . . ."

"To turn down our request," mourned Ensign Carnahan.

"We thought you might let us give Fritz one good dusting," echoed Ensign Chew.

"Stow the gab and listen, you noisy infants," rudely exclaimed Lieutenant Bevans. "I made up my mind today to give you a war flight. I expect to phone the British station tonight and arrange for a specified patrol area. You will be ready at daylight and the Lord have mercy on your souls."

The ensigns beamed and decorously refrained from cheering. They decided to turn in early and garner all the sleep possible, hoping the Boche planes might take a night off, but a visitor appeared in the person of a French ace on leave in Dunkirk. He was a sallow, low-spirited young man in spite of the honors emblazoned on his tunic—palms, stars, and crosses in incredible profusion. The conversation stumbled, because he spoke no English, but it was obvious that he regarded the war flight of the bold ensigns with a tinge of pessimism.

Their machine? He knew the type well. For active service it required aviators of profound experience. In the hands of beginners, alas, there had been many fatalities along the French coast. Flying far out over the sea was a different matter—here the resplendent ace shrugged a shoulder and his gesture was sinister. If only the Americans could wait for their own seaplanes with which they

were so much more familiar! Ceremoniously he wished
them good fortune, although plainly expecting the worst,
and stalked out into the gloom.

"A merry guy, that," murmured Ensign Carnahan, as he
smothered a yawn. "He will be all upset if we come back
alive. I hate to disappoint him."

"He had to begin, didn't he, Bob? These wise birds have
been at it so long that they can't remember anything else."

The weather next morning was uncommonly kind, a
bright sky with a light breeze which dispelled the Channel
mist. The French trawlers were plodding seaward to sweep
their appointed routes, and a division of British destroyers
fled from the harbor on some mysterious errand of their
own. Lieutenant Bevans inspected the seaplane with the
most scrupulous care before he ordered the waiting
squad of bluejackets to lower it from the slipway into the
basin. It was, in fact, a flying boat, with a whaleback hull
and a wingspread of eighty feet.

Ensign Carnahan crawled into the pilot's seat forward
and Al Chew tucked himself into the cockpit aft, where he
acted as observer and manipulated the machine gun. Upon
a chart were laid out their courses and bearings for the
patrol tour, and they had rejoiced to find that they were
to swing toward the Belgian coast, where there was always
the chance of encountering an enemy plane or two on
scouting duty. Sternly Lieutenant Bevans informed them
that they were not to go surging off in search of trouble. Air
combats were not their particular job. They were, first of
all, to patrol for enemy submarines and help safeguard the
lanes of merchant traffic. The ensigns blithely promised
obedience and then the roar of the propeller cut short the
farewells.

The graceful machine skittered over the surface of the
water, flinging clouds of spray, swiftly gathered flying

speed, and rose clear, climbing a thousand feet before it swerved to the northward. The engine sang powerfully without miss or falter. The two ensigns were buoyantly happy. No more than a few minutes had passed when they were able to descry the flat shore of Belgium, scarcely distinguishable from the sea, and the hazy mass of buildings and tall chimneys identified as Ostend. Mere specks against the sky, two enemy planes hovered above the enslaved city from whose harbor the German submarines crept out on their infamous business. Reluctantly Bob Carnahan steered wide to sweep farther away from the coast, toward the middle of Dover Strait. Bombing Ostend was the job of the squadrons of huge Handley-Page machines from the British station at Dunkirk, and they attended to it exceedingly well.

Keen-eyed, vigilant, the two ensigns scrutinized the sea which unrolled far beneath them like a brown carpet flecked with little flashes of foam, for once unvexed by boisterous winds. Crowded transports and grimy cargo boats were traversing the highway between England and France, moving in safety because the naval power of Germany was impotent to thwart them. Toylike, the fleets of drifters and destroyers steamed restlessly to and fro on the surface patrol. The ambushed U-boats, however, appeared to be engaged elsewhere, for there was never the glint of a periscope with the telltale furrow spreading in its wake, or the glimpse of a conning tower as it broke water.

An empty quest for the American air patrol, but such was the fortune of war, and one could not reasonably hope to bag a submarine every day! Before the eager ensigns realized it, they had been in the air two hours and soon they would have to be winging it back to port. The breeze was a trifle stronger, they noticed, and the sky had become overcast. This winter weather was apt to be treacherous.

Carnahan eyed the sodden cloud banks which were massing swiftly, and a gust brought a spatter of rain. He turned to wave a hand at his comrade in the rear cockpit, and Ensign Chew nodded assent. Another gale might be brewing in the Channel, and the rain and mist were apt to close down like a curtain.

Soon after the course was laid for Dunkirk, the coast became invisible, obscured in gray vapor, and Carnahan studied his compass with some slight uneasiness. Rapidly the task of holding the flying boat true to the proper bearings became more difficult. The wind had shifted so that it caught the sensitive craft on the beam instead of ahead, and she drifted away to leeward while the hull swayed and plunged to the lift and swoop of the wide wings. To ease the strain the pilot was compelled to steer dead into the wind whenever the sudden flurries whistled through the struts with a menacing note. Instead of holding a beeline for Dunkirk, the laboring craft was blown toward the wider reaches of the Channel, and the sense of direction was confused now that the landmarks were invisible.

The engine had behaved well until now, but the excessive vibration seemed to portend trouble. The boat was not new, and this ordeal of rough weather was testing every part to the uttermost. Carnahan was warned by the irregular pulsation of the motor, the break in the rhythm, and a perceptible loss of power. He could not leave his station, but Ensign Chew, also suspecting a mishap, was desperately attempting to investigate the engine while he hung on by his eyelids and displayed the agility of an acrobat. Presently the mechanical malady revealed alarming symptoms. The motor almost died and picked up again with a languid flutter. The craft coasted toward the sea in a long slant, recovered itself, flew on an even keel for a short distance, and again dipped downward.

Near at hand the water was seen to be perilously rough. There was no choice, however, and after a final struggle to climb clear, the unlucky cruiser, no longer a flying boat, poked her blunt nose into a white-crested wave and tried to submerge entirely.

The next sea washed over the hull, half filling it. The shock of the first impact was so violent that the two ensigns were pitched forward, and while they groped to recover themselves the salt water almost strangled them. Surprised at finding the old boat still intact and afloat, they sputtered and swore and baled furiously with canvas buckets. The boat was making a gallant battle for survival, breasting the waves more staunchly than the castaways had dared to hope. The motion was wild and dizzy, one wing dipping under while the other reared skyward, and the spray broke in sheets over the plunging hull, but the fragile structure somehow held together and refused to fill and founder.

Ensign Alfred Chew crawled forward, shook the water from helmet and goggles, and shouted in his shipmate's ear; "Are we downhearted? It was the gasoline feed pipe —cracked and then jarred off close to the pump. A clean break and there's no mending it. You can't tape it. And pitching about on our heads this way we can't get the bally thing apart."

"Right you are, Al. And never a vessel in sight to pick us up. The place was alive with them a little while ago. Better get a pigeon started right away."

The boat lacked radio equipment, but the two precious pigeons, although sadly bedraggled, had escaped drowning, and Ensign Chew extracted one from the small box and warmed and caressed it while Carnahan scribbled the message for help and slipped it into the aluminum cartridge, which they clasped on the bird's leg. It fluttered in a dazed manner when released, hovered over the drifting machine, flew in a zigzag course for a minute or two, and then sped in the direction of Dunkirk.

"We'll let the other one go in an hour or so if we are still messing about here," said Carnahan. "Fish out the Thermos bottle and the sandwiches, Al. In this thick weather we are liable to be hard to find."

They ate and drank with frugal care, reserving part of the emergency ration. Drenched and chilled to the bone, such exposure as this must soon exhaust their vitality. Huddled together in the forward cockpit, they began sending up distress signals, using green Very lights which, in clear weather, might have been visible for several miles. In this gray smother of mist and rain and spindrift, however, such signals were pitifully futile. The boat was wrenched and twisted by the immense leverage of wings, which yawed and tripped in an insane seesaw. It seemed as though they must be torn from the hull, leaving it to capsize. There was neither sight nor sound of shipping, and the steady pressure of the wind was carrying them down the Channel.

"That French ace with the chronic grouch didn't guess so far wrong," admitted Ensign Chew between his chattering teeth. "He was a Jonah. I didn't like his make-up."

"Aces?" exclaimed Carnahan with a feeble grin. "We are the original pair of two-spots. That dugout of ours looks like a cozy corner to me."

Talk was infrequent for some time after this. Shivering, benumbed, they baled the cockpit at intervals and stared into the gloomy weather, silently wondering how long they could hope to live through such a tragic ordeal as this. They were navy men, but with little experience afloat, and the wretched motion of their derelict craft afflicted them with seasickness. They were unspeakably miserable, too much so to be frightened.

The day wore on to noon. There was a bit of comfort in the fact that the seas grew no worse while the wind had sensibly diminished and the sky was less somber. Survivors of torpedoed merchant ships had suffered worse things in open boats, no doubt, or washed about on rafts for days, and this occurred to the two ensigns. They had no idea of whimpering, but were grimly hanging on. If the pigeons had reached Dunkirk, a vessel must have been sent out in haste, but nothing was seen of it.

"We have properly lost ourselves," said Carnahan, "and if we are picked up it will be a matter of sheer luck."

"A chilly proposition, if we have to make a night of it," replied young Chew, "but we'll stick on somehow."

The wind dropped to a harmless breeze and the sea was almost tranquil, but the wrecked seaplane floated soggily and the hull leaked like a basket. Carnahan was trying to calk a crack with strips of canvas and a pocketknife when his comrade clutched him by the arm and hoarsely implored him to look astern. Spellbound, they gazed and their mouths hung open. Ensign Alfred Chew rubbed his eyes and muttered strong language. Bob Carnahan clenched his fists and could find no words to fit his impassioned emotions.

Moving very slowly and protruding no more than two feet above the surface, a bit of metal pipe left a ripple in its wake. The upper end of it was an elbow into which was fitted a lens and the glitter of this glass disc suggested the living eye of some very formidable sea monster. It inspected the drifting seaplane and the forlorn passengers with a scrutiny deliberate and leisurely, with a cold-blooded, impersonal detachment, pausing when abreast of the American flag, which was painted on the yellow hull of the flying boat.

"You were so anxious to find a periscope, Bob," muttered Ensign Chew. "There it is, all right. What are you going to do with it?"

"Fritz is giving us the once-over, Al, old man. That can't be one of our own submarines or it would come up and hail us and show a little human interest. An interesting situation, isn't it?"

"You put it mildly. It is almost sensational. What's the idea? Will he stand by for the pleasure of seeing us drown, or will he ram our boat and finish the job at once?"

"You have another guess or two. He may pop up alongside and snatch us aboard as prisoners."

"I hadn't thought of that," dolefully replied the other ensign. "A couple of American naval officers might be considered good hunting. That doesn't appeal to me, Bob. This surrender stuff isn't taught in our service, not while your ship is afloat and under your feet."

"Here we are, with a pair of perfectly good hundred-pound bombs still hitched to our old scow and we can't drop them on Fritz," was Al's lament. "We might crumple his periscope with a burst from the machine gun."

"He would poke up another tube and then smash through us bows on. I wish he would either beat it or finish up his dirty work. I dislike being stared at. It makes me nervous."

The prowling U-boat had circled the crippled seaplane by this time, still submerged as though fearing a trap. Uncanny it was to watch the creeping periscope and to picture the German officer standing at the lower end of the long tube in the brilliantly lighted compartment, perhaps jesting at the plight of the Yankee aviators who had sworn to destroy the so-glorious submarines of the unconquerable *Vaterland*. It was this brutal, gloating delay that infuriated the two ensigns. They were being played with as a cat torments a mouse. The thing was unsportsmanlike, inhuman, and Bob Carnahan was in no mood for discretion.

"We lose, Al, either way we play it," he growled. "I'd sooner drown than throw up my hands to that dirty murderer. Crawl aft to the machine gun and we'll wait for his next move. By Jove, I believe he's coming up."

The submarine showed the dripping top of the conning tower, and presently the long deck heaved in sight, the water washing over it like a bit of reef. Bold against the gray paint stood out the lettering—"U-62." The unpleasant apparition fascinated the two ensigns. It was very much as though a bad dream had come true. For the moment they felt more curiosity than alarm. In all their glib talk of strafing Fritz it had not occurred to them that Fritz might take a hand at the game. He was not apt to feel kindly toward the Allied seaplanes which hunted and bombed him without mercy, earnestly seeking to blow him to kingdom come with all hands.

Ensign Chew had cuddled close to his machine gun. It was obvious that he yearned to let fly at the first close-cropped German head which should show itself above the screen of the tiny bridge on top of the conning tower. Bob Carnahan had learned to know his companion as an impulsive youth who was likely to let the consequences go hang, and he therefore shouted a caution to hold steady and avoid trouble until the enemy had shown his hand. The vindictive Chew scowled at the U-boat and glumly obeyed orders.

They heard the clang of metal as the round hatch plates were flung back, unsealing the submarine and opening an exit through the conning tower. There emerged into view a burly figure of a man in oilskins, who wore an officer's cap. Two sailors clambered up after him and rested their rifles upon the railing of the bridge. He raised the binoculars which hung from his neck by a strap and subjected the two castaways to critical inspection. Then he bawled through a megaphone; "I vill you alive take as prisoners. It is a kindness, so? I haf not forgetted the *King Stephen* trawler what left the crew of a Zeppelin to be drowned in the North Sea, but a German officer vas a gentleman always. He makes war not like the dishonorable English."

This was too much for the temper of Ensign Bob Carnahan, who threw up his head at the challenge and shouted back; "German gentlemen! Do you think we have forgotten the *Lusitania?*"

The florid face of the submarine commander turned a richer hue as he turned and said something to the two sailors who filled the small space beside him. They stood at attention, the rifles ready for action.

"Jump in the *wasser* and swim to my boat," was the command hurled at the American ensigns. The voice was harsh and unsteady with anger.

"We don't know how to swim," lied Al Chew. "You will have to send over and get us."

Carnahan had ceased to gaze at the submarine. His attention had shifted for the moment, but the horizon was still empty with nothing to indicate that a friendly vessel might intervene in time to save them. He was staring into the sea quite close at hand, but the uneasy waves merely disclosed a drifting bit of wood like a fragment of a spar. Tense and alert with some sudden excitement, he passed the word to the rear cockpit; "That's the way, Al. String him along. Play for time. Anything to keep him just where he is."

"What is the idea, Bob?"

"Never mind. I can't explain now, but there is about one chance in a hundred that we may be able to pull something off. Annoy the 'honorable German gentleman.' Insult him, and go as far as you like, but keep away from that machine gun unless he shoots first."

Again the submarine commander yelled the order to surrender by jumping into the sea, but the obstreperous Yankees persisted in debating the question. The U-boat carried a collapsible canvas skiff, argued Carnahan, and it was the plain duty of the captors to launch it and take off the prisoners, who were already exhausted and too feeble to stay afloat.

"But you haf life jackets on yourselves, stupids!" yelled the exasperated Teuton, as he snatched a rifle from a sailor and flourished it wildly.

"Filled with sawdust instead of cork! Yankee graft!" pleasantly explained Carnahan. "You have read your own newspapers, so you know all about it."

"How perfectly lovely!" applauded Ensign Chew from his end of the derelict. "The square-headed boob actually believes it. Better be ready to duck, Bob. He is sincerely peeved."

This diagnosis was accurate. Presumably to frighten them into prompt obedience, the irate commander threw up the rifle and pulled trigger. A bullet whistled over Carnahan's head and another drilled a hole in the coaming at his elbow. The result was totally unlooked for aboard the German submarine. Instead of diving into the sea with a cry of *Kamerad*, the impetuous Ensign Chew emitted a joyous war whoop. The enemy had opened fire on the American flag. Tradition knew but one reply, from John Paul Jones to David Farragut. So it appeared, at least, to young Alfred Chew as he instantaneously cleared for action and sighted the machine gun to sweep the bridge of the submarine. With a vicious rat-tat-tat a stream of bullets sought the mark.

The wrecked seaplane was an unsteady gun platform, which was all that saved the German commander and his two sailors from being so many perforated ruins. A tattered wing of the aircraft tripped in a wave just as the ensign fired, and the abrupt check marred his intentions. He shot a trifle low and the bullets spattered the conning tower. In a twinkling the bridge was vacant. It was incredible that a burly commander in oilskins and two sturdy German sailors could have vanished through the little round hatch without jamming together and sticking fast. By way of an encore, Ensign Chew fired another burst and lavishly punctuated the distasteful lettering—"U-62." The bullets rattled against the thin steel plating like pebbles on a tin roof.

"They can't pop out on deck again," hopefully observed the American gunner. "The lid is on that outfit. But I'm afraid I have spilled the beans, Bob, old man. You told me to sit tight and wait them out. I just couldn't help cutting loose when he tried to pot you."

"Thanks. I don't believe you have spoiled the show," Carnahan replied, with an unruffled mien. "We couldn't have beguiled him with conversation any longer. He turned nasty. You have bottled them up, sure enough. Not a man of them will dare to lift a hatch to get out and serve a gun. And they won't care to waste an expensive torpedo on us."

"He will ram us right away, then. Nothing doing with my machine gun. A can opener would be more useful."

Ensign Carnahan was again absorbed in staring at the water where the bit of painted wood still floated within range of his vision. The seaplane had drifted with the wind and the German submarine had forged a little way ahead, so that the relative positions were altered. The tossing fragment of spar, or whatever it was, now lay between the two crafts. Carnahan beckoned and Ensign Chew scrambled forward to join him. They paid no heed to the submarine which slowly gathered steerageway under power of her surface engines.

"Yes, Fritz will ram us," said Carnahan, as though thinking aloud, "but he isn't a bit anxious to drown the pair of us. He may be under orders, as I figure it out, to capture any American naval officers alive. He behaves that way, at any rate. So if he comes ahead to smash our old boat into kindling he will move at slow speed and then try to fish us up out of the wet."

"Good dope," agreed Ensign Chew. "That machine gun of ours makes it impossible for him to turn the trick in any other way. Too good to be true, Bob, but it does look to me as if we had a chance to win. You're bright."

"Watch it, Al! Look sharp! When the next wave breaks, just beyond the floating stick," breathlessly exclaimed Carnahan.

Close to the surface there appeared for an instant what looked like a string of croquet balls, for shape and size. They were linked together in some manner, rising, then dipping, invisible excepting for such a fleeting glimpse as this. The ensigns looked out to measure the course of the submarine which was turning in a wide arc to point her bow at the helpless seaplane. Yes, the stratagem of delay had been nicely timed. Wind and tide had set the three factors of the equation in the proper relative positions. Carnahan had maneuvered against hopeless odds, but the gods of chance were kind to him and the luck of the American Navy held good.

"Slow, Fritzie! Left rudder now, and then straight

ahead," implored Al Chew, his weather-cracked lips quivering with excitement.

"He can't miss it now," croaked Carnahan. "Our side is turned square toward him, and that's where he wants to hit and rip the old bus wide-open. I'll bet you a hundred even he never gets here."

"You're on, Bob. It would be a pleasure to lose. Here he comes, dead on the mark, and as wicked as sin!"

The long gray hull of the predatory U-boat was moving sluggishly while the sea frothed across the deck. It displayed no indications of human life or guidance. Monstrous, slinking, it profaned the brave and manly traditions of blue water. The youthful American officers, forgetting how cold and wet and fatigued they were, oblivious even of the grave peril that menaced them, watched the enemy draw near. They were, in fact, supremely happy, for this was the great adventure, the sporting chance.

"Supposing the scheme doesn't work," whispered Chew. "It may fail to connect."

"Then it's good night," said Carnahan. He gulped as he spoke.

The U-boat was drawing near the tossing bit of spar and that curious string of little globes fastened all in a row, which so closely resembled croquet balls. To the German commander and the helmsman behind the thick bull's-eye windows of the conning tower these harmless particles of flotsam were no doubt invisible. Undeviatingly the submarine held its course until the swaying, half-submerged row of balls were directly athwart the rounded bow. Bob Carnahan clasped his comrade around the neck and they danced in water up to their knees.

The nose of the submarine surged under between two waves and picked up the odd cluster of balls. They clung to the deck, instead of being washed off, and many more of them appeared, dragged from beneath the surface, fathom after fathom, all linked together in a meshwork of tarred cords. And attached to this system of floats was a vast net fashioned of wire cable, which had been suspended deep down in the sea. It trailed past the sides of the submarine and wrapped itself about the hull before the startled German commander could realize the danger or reverse his engines.

The net clung to its quarry like the tentacles of an octopus. It was strongly, cunningly fashioned, yet so light and pliant that it entangled itself with any moving object unlucky enough to encounter the trap. In this instance the net accomplished what was expected of it, for the submarine failed to check its headway until the whirling propellers had become wound up in the tenacious fabric. The predicament was precisely like that of a fly in a spider's web. To struggle was to make matters so much worse. The destruction of the wrecked seaplane had ceased to interest the German officers and crew.

"I win a hundred off you," cried Bob Carnahan, pounding his friend on the back. "We pulled it off—so far—but here's hoping and praying for the second act."

"If he has sense enough to stay quiet, just as he is, the beggar can set his men to hacking away with axes and maybe clear himself," anxiously suggested Ensign Chew. "I guess I had better put a crimp in that little stunt."

He hastily returned to his machine gun and trained it on the conning tower, thereby anticipating the movements of the German crew. One of them cautiously raised his head above the bridge screen, and young Chew riddled the strip of canvas with a rattling fusillade. It was to be conjectured that exposure of this kind was indubitably fatal. The attempt to gain the deck was unanimously abandoned.

"We have bagged a submarine, but we don't know what

to do with it," complained Carnahan. "I might swim over and ask them to surrender, but what's the use? I am still expecting the grand finale, but it seems to be delayed or something."

"He will fill his tanks and submerge," argued Chew. "He can drop down forty or fifty feet and let the sweep of the tide carry him clear of us and our nifty machine gun. Then he can come up and try to cut himself clear, or maybe he'll sit on the bottom till dark."

"If he doesn't drag the little spar buoy under with him he will be out of luck. It will give our surface patrols a clue to locate him. The buoy caught my eye first thing. That was how I happened to look for the net. I saw the Admiralty shops at Dover where they manufacture the stuff—went all through them with a British Navy pal."

They beheld the baffled U-boat sink lower until the deck had vanished and the conning tower was lapped by the sea. With negative buoyancy established, the commander risked starting his motors in order that a thrust ahead might give his boat a downward slant and so carry her to the desired depth. Possibly he hoped that the screws might thresh themselves clear of the enveloping net. Apparently the attempt was successful. The conning tower, then the slender periscopes, moving slowly, were seen to pass from sight, and the sea boiled white to mark the plunge.

Ensign Carnahan sighed, ungratefully ignoring the fact that he had just gained his liberty and perhaps his life.

"Wouldn't that break your heart, Al? He belonged to us. You see, I felt absolutely certain that he was going to blow himself up—once he ran afoul of that net. The British have invented a new mine for this special purpose—a cute little package of TNT which is tied to the bottom of the nets, about fifty feet apart. They explode on contact. I watched a hundred women putting them together in Dover. Maybe this net of ours had no mines on it. If a U-boat so much as touches one of these contraptions when she gets wrapped up in a net, it's—"

A terrific explosion flung the two young men headlong. The concussion fairly lifted the waterlogged hull of the seaplane. It simply fell apart like a watermelon dropped on a pavement. Bewildered, the two ensigns found themselves swimming amid the wreckage. Freed of the weight of the engine, a side of the boat came bobbing up and floated as a raft to which Carnahan clung. Chew attached himself to a part of the bow in which the air chamber was intact. They lashed these fragments together and managed to haul their bodies half out of water. During this struggle for existence they were conscious that the sea was tremendously agitated, churned into muddy whirlpools which subsided in greasy combers that rolled without breaking. The air reeked with the heavy smell of crude oil, and a dirty litter of debris was smeared over a slowly spreading area.

Bob Carnahan dashed the spray from his eyes and vainly looked for survivors of the U-62. It was Ensign Chew who first caught sight of a body, which was washing past him no more than a dozen yards distant. Dead, of course, he concluded, but one arm seemed to move of its own volition and the man was floating face upward. The ensign recognized the commander of the lost submarine and swam to reach him. Carnahan splashed in his wake and together they supported the insensible German until he could be towed to the rude raft and lifted thereupon. His head was badly gashed and he breathed ever so feebly, but there was life in him.

Fortunately, the succor so long delayed was now close at hand. The castaways could not have lived through another hour in this icy water. They had come to the end of

their strength. It was a British destroyer that sighted them
and approached cautiously, as though picking a course, instead of tearing along at its usual foaming gait. A boat was
lowered and the sympathetic seamen were about to lift
Ensign Bob Carnahan over the gunwale, when he hoarsely
protested, "The prisoner first, if you please, and be mighty
careful of him. He is the net result."

Whisked aboard the destroyer, the two ensigns were
thawed out beside the wardroom stove. The skipper insisted that they be tucked into bed, but they politely refused, and in borrowed clothes they told their won-
drous yarn to a group of rosy young officers.

"We have been looking for you all over the place,"
explained one of them. "A pigeon of yours got back to
Dunkirk. You drifted a lot, I presume, and—er—we never
dreamed of finding you just here, don't you know."

"My message may have given the wrong bearings," Carnahan admitted with a blush. "I wasn't quite sure of my
position after the weather turned so thick and squally.
Just where were we when you found us, may I ask?"

The destroyer officers appeared highly amused at this,
and the navigator chuckled as he explained, "Inside the
net barrage that was laid to catch the Huns if they try to go
down Channel. We were keeping clear of it, do you see,
when we heard an explosion—"

"That was U-62. We noticed it ourselves," said Ensign
Alfred Chew.

"Right-o. The blighter must have touched off a mine
when he was messing about in the nets. That is the trick of
it. And you chaps actually coaxed him into blowing himself to blazes! My word! How extraordinarily clever!"

"Carnahan did it," modestly affirmed Ensign Chew.

"Snappy work with the machine gun really did the business for Fritz," loyally exclaimed Bob. "It got his goat, and then we had him where we wanted him."

Before the hurrying destroyer reached Dunkirk the surgeon reported that the captured commander of U-62 would probably recover from his injuries. He had already revived and was able to talk a little. It was to be inferred that he held an extremely low opinion of a nation which would employ such dastardly contrivances against the gallant submarines of the Imperial German Navy. As for the Yankee aviators, he regretted that he had not sunk them at sight instead of behaving too gently and honorably.

Lieutenant Chuck Bevans, weary with the day's work, was at the mooring berth when the destroyer slipped into the basin. Darkness had fallen over the shattered, melancholy seaport of Dunkirk. The good news had been sent him by radio, and as his haggard but exultant brace of youngsters limped out the gangway he shook hands with them, and exclaimed, "Well done! These Britishers credit you with the destruction of a big, seagoing sub. It means a decoration or two. But I am glad to get you back alive and kicking. I cursed myself all day for letting you go."

"There was no need of worrying about us," grandly replied Ensign Carnahan. "We had a perfectly bully time, didn't we, Al?"

"You said it for me, Bob. This is the end of a perfect day."

They trudged in the direction of their humble quarters among the stone quays and passed the long, low mound with the roof of sandbags and boiler plate. In all likelihood they would be scrambling into the dugout a few hours later, for the sky had cleared and the stars were out.

"This is home, sweet home," murmured Ensign Carnahan, "and it's plenty good enough for me. I surely do pity the poor guys in the service who can't get overseas duty."

Ensign Alfred Chew breathed a long sigh of content-ment. With a glance at the shining stars overhead, he responded, "Well, if the old Boche comes over tonight, I think we have given him a pretty fair excuse for bombing us."

The Wildcat

BY ALBERT PAYSON TERHUNE

When Cassius Wyble came down from his mountains to the 2000-population metropolis of Clayburg on his half-yearly trip for supplies, he thought the old custom of Muster Day had been revived. No fewer than eleven men in khaki were lounging round the station platform or sitting on the steps of the North America general store. Enlistment posters, too, flared from windows and walls.

These posters—except for their pretty pictures—meant nothing at all to Cash Wyble. For, as with his parents and grandparents, his knowledge of the written or printed word was purely a matter of hearsay.

Yet the sight of the eleven men in newfangled uniform —so like in color to his own butternut homespuns—interested Cash. "What's all the boys doin'—togged up that-away?" he demanded of the North America's proprietor. "Waitin' for the band?"

"Waiting to be shipped to Camp Lee," answered the local merchant prince, adding, as Cash's burnt-leather face grew blanker, "Camp Lee, down in Virginia, you know. Training camp for the war."

"War?" queried Cash, preparing to grin, at prospect of a joke. "What war?"

"What war?" echoed the dumfounded storekeeper. "Why, *the* war, of course! Where in blazes have you been keeping yourself?"

"I been up home, where I belong," said Cash sulkily. "What with the hawgs, an' crops an' skins an' sich, a busy man's got no time traipsin' off to the city every minute. Twice a year does me pretty nice. An' now suppose you tell me what war you're blattin' about."

The storekeeper told him. He told him in the simplest possible language. Yet half—and more than half—of the explanation went miles above the listening mountaineer's head. Cash gathered, however, that the United States was fighting Germany.

Germany he knew by repute for a country or a town on the far side of the world. Some of its citizens had even invaded his West Virginia mountains, where their odd diction and porcelain pipes roused much derision among the cultured hill folk.

"Germany?" mused Cash, when the narrative was ended. "We're to war with Germany, hey? Sakes, but I wished I'd knowed that yesterday! A couple of Germans went right past my shack. I could 'a' shot 'em as easy as toad pie."

The North America's proprietor valued Cash Wyble's sparse trade, as he valued that of other mountaineers who made Clayburg their semiannual port of call. If on Cash's report these rustics should begin a guerilla warfare upon their German neighbors, more of them would presently be lodged in jail than the North America could well afford to spare from its meager customer list.

Wherefore the proprietor did some more explaining. Knowing the mountaineer brain, he made no effort to point out the difference between armed Germans and noncombatants. He merely said that the government had threatened to lock up any West Virginian who should kill a German—this side of Europe. It was a new law, he continued, and one that the revenue officers were bent on enforcing.

Cash sighed and reluctantly bade farewell to an alluring dream that had begun to shape itself in his simple brain— a dream of "laying out" in cliff-top brush, waiting with true elephant patience until a German neighbor should stroll, unsuspecting, along the trail below and should move slowly within range of the antique Wyble rifle.

It was a sweet fantasy, and hard to banish. For Cash certainly could shoot. There was scarce a man in the Cumberlands or the Appalachians who could outshoot him. Shooting and a native knack at moonshining were Cash's only real accomplishments. Whether stalking a shy old stag or potting a revenue officer on the sky line, the man's aim was uncannily true. In a region of born marksmen his skill stood forth supreme.

He felt not the remotest hatred for any of these local Germans. In an impersonal way he rather liked one or two of them. Yet, if the law had really been off. . . .

The zest of the man hunt tingled pleasantly in the marksman's blood. And he resented this unfair new revenue ruling, which permitted and even encouraged the killing of Germans in Europe and yet ordained a closed season on them in West Virginia. Still, there was no sense in a busy man's risking jail or a fine by indulging his sporting tastes. So Cash tried to forget the temptation, and proceeded to the more material task of trafficking for his next half year's supplies.

A few months later the draft caught Cash Wyble and carried him away in its swirling flood, depositing him in due time, with a quantity of similar mountaineer flotsam, in the training mill of Camp Lee.

No half-grown wildcat dragged by the scruff of the neck from the sanctuary of its tree hole was ever one tenth so ragingly indignant as was Cash at his impressment into his country's service. Born and bred of fellow illiterates in the wildest corner of the Cumberland Range, thirty-two miles from the nearest railroad, he knew nothing and cared less about the affairs of the world that lay beyond the circling blue mountain walls.

To Cash all persons who lived outside that circle were foreigners, even if their habitat was the adjoining county of his own state. He had heard of England and of France and of Europe, in much the same vague fashion as he had heard of Germany. He knew the name of the President of the United States; of the governor of West Virginia; of the mayor of Clayburg. Also of the political party whose ticket his father had always voted, and which Cash, in consequence, voted. He knew there had been a Civil War and—from pictures and from paternal description—he knew the types of uniforms each side had worn. The foregoing facts comprised his total knowledge of American politics and of world history.

As to the causes and the occasion and the stakes of the present war, he had not an inkling. Nor could the explanations of slightly better-informed recruits make the matter much clearer to him. It most certainly roused no trace of enthusiasm or of patriotism in his indignant breast. All he knew or was interested in was that he had been forced to leave his shack and his straggly mountainside farm and his hidden moonshine still, at the very worst possible season for leaving any of them.

He had been coerced into riding innumerable miles to a foreign state that seemed all bottom land, and there was herded with more men than he had known were on earth. He had been dressed in an amazing suit; made to wear socks and underclothes for the first time in his life; and daily put through a series of physical evolutions whose import was a sealed book to him. In all weathers, too, he must wear shoes.

Like the aforesaid caught wildcat, Cash Wyble rebelled at every inch of the way. For his first two months of captivity he spent more time in the guardhouse than out of it. On his first day at camp he tried to thrash a lieutenant who was lining up a rawly shambling company and who spoke with unwelcomed sharpness to the mountaineer. Scarce had Cash atoned for this crime when he succeeded in giving a very creditable thrashing to a sergeant who was teaching his squad the mysteries of about face.

Hearing that the nearby city of Petersburg was larger than Clayburg—which he knew to be the biggest metropolis in America—Cash set out to nail the lie by a personal inspection of Petersburg. He neglected to apply for leave, so was held up by the first sentinel he met.

Cash explained very politely his reason for quitting camp. But the pigheaded sentinel still refused to let him pass. Two minutes later a fast-summoned corporal and two men were using all their strength to pry Wyble loose from the luckless sentry. And again the guardhouse had Cash as a transient and blasphemous guest.

He was learning much more of kitchen-police work than of guard mount. At the latter task he was a failure. The first night he was assigned to beat pacing, the relief found him restfully snoring, on his back, his rifle stuck up in front of him by means of his bayonet thrust into the ground. Cash had seen no good reason why he should walk to and fro for hours when there was nothing exciting to watch for and when he had been awake since early morning. Therefore he had gone to sleep. And his subsequent guardhouse stay filled him with uncomprehending fury.

The salute, too, struck him as the height of absurdity— as a bit of tomfoolery in which he would have no part. Not that he was exclusive, but what was the use of touching one's forelock to some officer one had never before met? He was willing to nod pleasantly and even to say "Howdy, Cap?" when his company captain passed by him for the first time in the morning. But he saw no use in repeating that or any other form of salutation when the same captain chanced to meet him a bare fifteen minutes later.

Cash Wyble's case was not in any way unique among Camp Lee's thirty thousand new soldiers. Hundreds of mountaineers were in still worse mental plight. And the tact as well as the skill of their officers was strained wellnigh to the breaking point in shaping the amorphous backwoods rabble into trim soldiers.

Not all members of the mountain draft were so fiercely resentful as was Cash. But many others of them were like unbroken colts. The strange frequency of washing and of shaving, and the wearing of underclothes were their chief puzzles.

The company captain labored with Cash again and again, pointing out the need of neat cleanliness, of promptitude, of vigilance; trying to make him understand that a salute is not a sign of servility; seeking to imbue him with the spirit of patriotism and of discipline. But to Cash the whole thing was infinitely worse and more bewildering than had been the six months he had once spent in Clayburg jail for mayhem.

Three things alone mitigated his misery at Camp Lee: the first was the shooting; the second was his monthly pay —which represented more real money than he ever had had in his pocket at any one time; the third was the food— amazing in its abundance and luxurious variety to the always-hungry mountaineer.

But presently the target shooting palled. As soon as he had mastered carefully the intricacies of the queer new rifle they gave him, the hours at the range were no more inspiring to him than would be, to Paderewski, the eternal playing of the scale of C with one finger.

To Cash, the target shooting was child's play. Once he grasped the rules as to sights and elevations and became used to the feel of the army rifle, the rest was drearily simple. He could outshoot practically every man at Camp Lee. This gave him no pride. He made himself popular with men who complimented him on it by assuring them modestly that he outshot them not because he was such a dead shot but because they shot so badly.

The headiest colt in time will learn the lesson of the breaking pen. And Cash Wyble gradually became a soldier. At least he learned the drill and the regulations and how to keep out of the guardhouse—except just after payday; and his lank figure took on a certain military spruceness.

But under the surface he was still Cash Wyble. He behaved, because there was no incentive at the camp that
made disobedience worth while.

Then after an endless winter came the journey to the
seaboard and the embarkation for France; and the awe-
some sight of a tossing gray ocean a hundred times wider
and rougher than Clayburg River in freshet time. Followed a week of agonized terror, mingled with an acute
longing to die. Then ensued a week of calm water, during
which one might refill the oft-emptied inner man.

A few days later Cash was bumping along a newly re-
paired French railway in a car whose announced capacity
was forty men or eight horses. And thence to billet in a
half-wrecked village, where his regiment was drilled and
redrilled in the things they had toiled so hard at Camp Lee
to master, and in much that was novel to the men.

Cash next came to a halt in a network of trenches over-
looking a stretch of country that had been tortured into
hideousness—a region that looked like a Doré nightmare.
It was a waste of hillocks and gullies and shell holes and
blasted big trees and frayed copses and split boulders and
seared vegetation. When Cash heard it was called no man's
land he was not surprised. He well understood why no
man—not even an ignorant foreigner—cared to buy such a
tract.

He was far more interested in hearing that a tangle of
trenches, somewhat like his regiment's own, lay three miles
northeastward, at the limit of no man's land, and that those
trenches were infested with Germans.

Germans were the people Cash Wyble had come all the
way to France to kill. And once more the thrill of the man
hunt swept pleasantly through his blood. He had no desire
to risk prison. So he had made very certain by repeated in-
quiry that this particular section of France was in Europe;

and that no part of it was within the boundaries or the jurisdiction of the sovereign state of West Virginia. Here, therefore, the law was off on Germans, and he could not get into the slightest trouble with the hated revenue officers by shooting as many of the foe as he could go out and find.

Cash enjoyed the picture he conjured up—a picture of a whole bevy of Germans seated at ease in a trench, smoking porcelain pipes and conversing with one another in comically broken English; of himself stealing toward them, and from the shelter of one of those hillock boulders opening a mortal fire on the unsuspecting foreigners.

It was a quaint thought, and one that Cash loved to play with. Also it had an advantage that most of Cash's vivid mind pictures had not. For, in part, it came true.

The Germans, on the thither side of no man's land, seemed bent on jarring the repose and wrenching the nerve of their lately arrived Yankee neighbors. Not only were those veteran official entertainers, Minnie and Bertha, and their equally vocal artillery sisters called into service for the purpose, but a dense swarm of snipers were also impressed into the task.

Now this especial reach of no man's land was a veritable snipers' paradise. There was cover—plenty of it—everywhere. A hundred sharpshooters of any scouting prowess at all could deploy at will amid the tumble of boulders and knolls and twisted tree trunks and battered foliage and craters.

The long spell of wet weather had precluded the burning away of undergrowth. There were treetops and hill summits whence a splendid shot could be taken at unwary Americans in the lower front-line trenches and along the rising ground at the rear of the Yankee lines. Yes, it was a stretch of ground laid out for the joy of snipers. And the

German sharpshooters took due advantage of this bit of luck. The whine of a high-power bullet was certain to follow the momentary exposure of any portion of khaki anatomy above or behind the parapets. And in disgustingly many instances the bullet did not whine in vain. All of which kept the newcomers from getting any excess joy out of trench life.

To mitigate the annoyance there was a call for volunteer sharpshooters to scout cautiously through no man's land and seek to render the Boche sniping a less safe and exhilarating sport than thus far it had been. The job was full of peril, of course. For there was a more than even chance of the Yankee snipers' being sniped by the rival sharpshooters, who were better acquainted with the ground.

Yet at the first call there was a clamorous throng of volunteers. Many of these volunteers admitted under pressure that they knew nothing of scout work and that they had not so much as qualified in marksmanship. But they craved a chance at the Boche. And grouchily did they resent the swift weeding-out process that left their services uncalled for.

Cash Wyble was the first man accepted for the dangerous detail. And for the first time since the draft had caught him his burnt-leather face expanded into a grin that could not have been wider unless his flaring ears had been set back.

With two days' rations and a goodly store of cartridges he fared forth that night into no man's land. Dawn was not yet fully gray when the first crack of his rifle was wafted back to the trenches. Then the artillery firing, which was part of the day's work, set in. And its racket drowned the noise of any shooting that Cash might be at.

Forty-eight hours passed. At dawn of the third day Cash

came back to camp. He was tired and horribly thirsty; but his lantern-jawed visage was one unmarred mask of bliss.

"Twelve," he reported tersely to his captain. "At least," he continued in greater detail, "twelve that I'm dead sure of. Nice big ones, too, some of 'em."

"Nice big ones!" repeated the captain in admiring disgust. "You talk as if you'd been after wild turkeys!"

"A heap better'n wild-turkey shootin'!" said Cash with a grin. "An' I got twelve that I'm sure of. There was one, though, I couldn't get. A he-one, at that. He's sure some German, that feller! He's as crafty as they make 'em. I couldn't ever come up to him or get a line on him. I'll bet I throwed away thirty cartridges on just that one Dutchy. An' by-an'-by he found out what I was after. Then there was fun, Cap! Him and I did have one fine shootin' match! But I was as good at hidin' as he was. And there couldn't neither one of us seem to get to the other. Most of the rest of 'em was as easy to get as a settin' hen. But not him. I'd 'a' laid out there longer for a crack at him, but I couldn't find no water. If there'd been a spring or a water seep anywheres there I'd 'a' stayed till doomsday but what I'd 'a' got him. Soon's I fill up with some water I'm goin' back after him. He's well worth it. I'll bet that cuss don't weigh an ounce under two hundred pound."

Cash's smug joy in his exploit and his keen anticipation of a return trip were dashed by the captain's reminder that war is not a hunting jaunt; and that Wyble must return to his loathed trench duties until such time as it should seem wise to those above him to send him forth again.

Cash could not make head or tail out of such a command. After months of grinding routine he had at last found a form of recreation that not only dulled his sharply constant homesickness, but that made up for all he had gone through. And now he was told he could go forth on such delightful excursions only when he might chance to be sent!

Red wrath boiled hot in the soul of Cash Wyble. Experience had taught him the costly folly of venting such rage on a commissioned officer. So he hunted up Top Sergeant Mahan of his own company and laid his griefs before that patient veteran.

Top Sergeant Mahan—formerly of the regular army— listened with true sympathy to the complaint; and listened with open enthusiasm to the tale of the two days of forest skulking. But he could offer no help in the matter of returning to the battue.

"The cap'n was right," declared Mahan. "They wanted to throw a little lesson into those Boche snipers and make them ease up on their heckling. And you gave them a man's-size dose of their own physic. There's not one sniper out there today, to ten who were on deck three days ago. You've done your job. And you've done it good and plenty. But it's done—for a while anyhow. You weren't brought over here to spend your time in prowling round no man's land on a still hunt for stray Germans. That isn't Uncle Sam's way. Don't go grouching over it, man! You'll be remembered, all right. And if they get pesky again, you'll be the first one sent out to abate them. You can count on it. Till then, go ahead with your regular work and forget the sniper job."

"But, Sarge!" pleaded Cash, "you don't get the idea. You don't get it at all. Those Germans will be shyer than scat, now that I've flushed 'em. An' the longer the news has a chance to get around among 'em, the shyer they're due to get. Why, even if I was to go out there straight off it ain't likely I'd be able to pot one where I potted three before. It's the same difference as it is between the first flushin' of a wild-turkey bunch an' the second. An' if I've got to wait long there'll be no downin' *any* of 'em. Tell that to the cap. Make him see if he wants them cusses he better let me get 'em while they're still gettable."

In vain did Top Sergeant Mahan go over and over the same ground, trying to make Cash see that the company captain and those above him were not out for a record in the matter of ambushed Germans.

Wyble had struck one idea he could understand, and he would not give it up. "But, Sarge," he urged desperately, "I'm no good here foolin' around with drill an' relief an' diggin' an' all that. Any mudback can do them things if you folks is set on havin' 'em done. But there ain't another man in all this outfit who can shoot like I can; or has the knack of 'layin' out'; or of stalkin'. Pop got the trick of it from Grandfather. An' Grandfather got it off the Injuns in the old days. If you folks is out to get Germans I'm the feller to git 'em for you. Nice big ones. If you're here just to play soldier, any poor fool can play it for you as good as me."

"I've just told you," began the sergeant, "that we—"

"Another thing!" suggested Cash brightly. "These Germans must have villages somewheres. All folks do. Even Injuns. Some place where they live when they ain't on the warpath. Get leave an' rations an' cartridges for me—for a week, or maybe two—an' I'll guarantee to scout till I find one of them villages. The Dutchies won't be expectin' me. An' I can likely pot a whole mess of 'em before they can get to cover.

"Say!" he went on eagerly, a bit of general information flashing into his memory. "Did you know Germans was a kind of Confed? The fightin' Germans, I mean. Well, they are. The whole twelve I got was dressed in Gray Confed uniform, same as Pop used to wear. I got his old uniform

to home. Lord, but Pop would sure lay into me if he
knowed I was pepperin' his old side partners like that! I'd
figured that all Germans was dressed like the ones back
home. But they've got regular uniforms. Confed uniforms,
at that. I wonder does our general know about it?"

Again the long-suffering Mahan tried to set him right;
this time as to the wide divergence between the gray-
backed troops of Ludendorff and the Confederacy's gallant soldiers. But Cash merely nodded cryptically, as always he did when he thought his foreigner fellow soldiers
were trying to take advantage of his supposed ignorance.
And he swung back to the theme nearest his heart.

"Now about that snipin' business," he pursued, "even if
the cap don't want too many of 'em shot up, he sure won't
be so cantankerous as to keep me from tryin' to get that
thirteenth feller! I mean the one that kept blazin' at me
whiles I kept blazin' at him; an' the both of us too cute to
show an inch of target to the other or stay in the same
patch of cover after we'd fired. That Dutchy sure can scout
grand! He's a born woodsman. An' you all don't want it to
be said the Germans has got a better sniper than what
we've got, do you? Well, that's just what will be said by
everyone in this here county unless you let me down him.
Come on, Sarge! Let me go back after him! I been thinkin'
up a trick Grandfather got off of the Injuns. It oughter
land him sure. Let me go try! I believe that feller can't
weigh an ounce less than two twenty. Leave me have one
more go after him; and I'll bring him in to prove it!"

Top Sergeant Mahan's patience stopped fraying, and
ripped from end to end. "You seem to think this war is a
cross between a mountain feud and a deer hunt!" he
growled. "Isn't there any way of hammering through your
mind that we aren't here to pick off unsuspecting Germans

and make a tally of the kill? And we aren't here to brag
about the size of the men we shoot, either. We're here,
you and I, to obey orders and do our work. You'll get
plenty of shooting before you go home again, don't worry.
Only you'll do it the way you're told to. After all the time
you've spent in the hoosegow since you joined, I should
think you'd know that."

But Cash Wyble did not know it. He said so—loudly,
offensively, blasphemously. He said many things—things
that in any other army than his own would have landed
him against a blank wall facing a firing squad. Then he
slouched off by himself to grumble.

As far as Cash Wyble was concerned the war was a
failure—a total failure. The one bright spot in its worka-
day monotony was blurred for him by the orders of his
stupid superiors. In his vivid imagination that elusive German sniper gradually attained a weight not far from three
hundred pounds.

In sour silence Cash sulked through the rest of the day's
routine. In his heart boiled black rebellion. He had learned
his soldier trade, back at Camp Lee, because it had been
very strongly impressed upon him that he would go to jail
if he did not. For the same reason he had not tried to
desert. He had all the true mountaineer horror for prison.
He had toned down his native temper and stubbornness,
because failure to do so always landed him in the guardhouse—a place that, to his mind, was almost as terrible as
jail.

But out here in the wilderness there were no jails. At
least Cash had seen none. And he had it on the authority
of Top Sergeant Mahan himself that this part of France
was not within the legal jurisdiction of West Virginia—the
only region, as far as Cash actually knew, where men are

put in prison for their misdeeds. Hence the rules governing Camp Lee could not be supposed to obtain out here. All of which comforted Cash not a little.

To him *patriotism* was a word as meaningless as was *discipline*. The law of force he recognized—the law that had hog-tied him and flung him into the army. But the higher law which makes men risk their all, right blithely, that their country and civilization may triumph—this was as much a mystery to Cash Wyble as to any army mule.

Just now he detested the country that had dragged him away from his lean shack and forbade him to disport himself as he chose in no man's land. He hated his country; he hated his army; he hated his regiment. Most of all he loathed his captain and Top Sergeant Mahan.

At Camp Lee he had learned to comport himself more or less like a civilized recruit, because there was no breach of discipline worth the penalty of the guardhouse. Out here it was different.

That night Private Cassius Wyble got hold of two other men's emergency rations, a bountiful supply of water, and a stuffing pocketful of cartridges. With these and his adored rifle he eluded the sentries—a ridiculously easy feat for so skilled a woodsman—and went over the top and on into no man's land.

By daylight he had trailed and potted a German sniper. By sunrise he had located the man against whom he had sworn his strategy feud—the German who had put him on his mettle two days before.

Cash did not see his foe. And when from the edge of a rock he fired at a puff of smoke in a clump of trees no resultant body came tumbling earthward. And thirty seconds later a bullet from quite another part of the clump spatted hotly against the rock edge five inches from his head. Cash smiled beatifically. He recognized the tactics of his former opponent. And once more the merry game was on.

To make perfectly certain of his rival's identity, Cash wiggled low in the undergrowth until he came to a jut of rock about seven feet long and two feet high. Lying at full length behind this low barrier, and parallel to it, Cash put his hat on the toe of his boot and cautiously lifted his foot until the hat's sugar-loaf crown protruded a few inches above the top of the rock.

On the instant, from the tree clump, snapped the report of a rifle. The bullet, ignoring the hat, nicked the rock comb precisely above Cash's upturned face. He nodded approval, for it told him that his enemy was not only a good forest fighter but that he recognized the same skill in Wyble.

Thus began two days of delightful pastime for the ex-iled mountaineer. Thus, too, began a series of offensive and defensive maneuvers worthy of Natty Bumppo and Old Sleuth combined.

It was not until Cash abandoned the hunt long enough to find and shoot another German sniper and appropriate the latter's uniform that he was able, under cover of dusk, to get near enough to the tree clump for a fair sight of his antagonist. At which juncture a snap shot from the hip ended the duel.

Cash's initial thrill of triumph, even then, was dampened. For the sniper—to whom by this time he had credited the size of Goliath, at the very least—proved to be a wizened little fellow, not much more than five feet tall.

Still Cash had won. He had outgeneraled a mighty clever sharpshooter. He had gotten what he came out for, and two other snipers, besides. It was not a bad bag. As there was nothing else to stay there for, and as his water was gone, as well as nearly all his cartridges, Cash shoul-

dered his rifle and plodded wearily back to camp for a
night's rest.

There, to his amazed indignation, he was not received
as a hero, even when he sought to recount his successful
adventures. Instead, he was arrested at once on a charge
of technical desertion, and was lodged in the local substi-
tute for a regular guardhouse.

Bewildered wrath smothered him. What had he done,
to be arrested again? True, he had left camp without
leave. But had he not atoned for this peccadillo fiftyfold
by the results of his absence? Had he not killed three men
whose business it was to shoot Americans? Had he not
killed the very best sniper the Germans could hope to
possess?

Yet, they had not promoted him. They had not so much
as thanked him. Instead, they had stuck him here in the
hoosegow. And Mahan had said something about a court-
martial.

It was black ingratitude! That was what it was. That
and more. Such people did not deserve to have the services of a real fighter like himself. Which started another
train of thought.

Apparently—except on special occasions—the Americans did not send men out into the wilderness to take pot
shots at the lurking foe. And apparently that was just what
the Germans always did. He had full proof, indeed, of the
German custom. For had he not found a number of the
graybacks thus happily engaged? Not for one occasion
only, but as a regular thing?

Yes, the Germans had sense enough to appreciate a good
fighter when they had one. And they knew how to make
use of him in a way to afford innocent pleasure to himself
and much harm to the enemy. That was the ideal life for
a soldier—"laying out" and sniping the foe. Not kitchen-

police work and endless drill and digging holes and taking baths. Sniping was the job for a he-man, if one had to be away from home at all. And in the German ranks alone was such happy employment to be found.

When Cash calmly and definitely made up his mind to desert to the Germans, he was troubled by no scruples at all. Even the dread of the mysterious court-martial added little weight to his decision. The deed seemed to him not a whit worse than was the leaving of one farmer's employ, back home, to take service with another who offered more congenial work. Wherefore, he deserted.

It was not at all difficult for him to escape from the elementary cell in which he was confined. It was a mere matter of strategy and luck. So was his escape to no man's land.

Unteroffizier Otto Schrabstaetter an hour later conducted to his company commander a lanky and leather-faced man in khaki uniform, who had accosted a sentry with the pacific plea that he be sworn in as a member of the German Army.

The sentry did not know English; nor did Unteroffizier Otto Schrabstaetter. And though Cash addressed them both in a very fair imitation of the gutteral English he had heard used by the West Virginia Germans—and which he fondly believed to be pure German—they did not understand a word of his plea. So he was taken to the captain, a man who had lived for five years in New York.

With the Unteroffizier at his side and with two armed soldiers just behind him, Cash confronted the captain, and under the latter's volley of barked questions told his story. Ten minutes afterward he was repeating the same tale to a flint-faced man with a fox-brush mustache—Colonel von Scheurer, commander of the regiment that held that section of the first-line trench.

A little to Cash's aggrieved surprise, neither the captain

nor the colonel seemed interested in his prowess as a sharpshooter or in his ill-treatment at the hands of his own army.
Instead, they asked an interminable series of questions that
seemed to have no bearing at all on his case.

They wanted, for instance, to know the name of his regiment; its quota of men; how long they had been in France;
what sea route they had taken in crossing the ocean; from
what port they had sailed; and the approximate size of the
convoy. They wanted to know what regiments lay to either
side of Cash's in the American trenches; how many men
per month America was sending overseas and where they
usually landed. They wanted to know a thousand things
more, of the same general nature.

Cash saw no reason why he should not satisfy their silly
curiosity. And he proceeded to do so to the best of his
ability. But as he did not know so much as the name of the
port whence he had shipped to France, and as the rest of
his tactical knowledge was on the same plane, the fast-
barked queries presently took on a tone of exasperation.

This did not bother Cash. He was doing his best. If these
people did not like his answers that was no affair of his.
He was here to fight, not to talk. His attention wandered.

Presently he interrupted the colonel's most searching
questions to ask, "You all don't happen to be the Kaiser, do
you? I suppose not though. I'll bet that old Kaiser must
weigh. . . ."

A thundered oath brought him back to the subject at
hand, and the cross-questioning went on. But all the queries elicited nothing more than a mass of misinformation,
delivered with such palpable genuineness of purpose that
even Colonel von Scheurer could not doubt the man's good
faith. And at last the two officers began to have a very fair
estimate of the mountaineer's character and of the reasons
that had brought him thither.

Still it was the colonel's mission in life to suspect—to take nothing for granted. And after all, this yokel and his queer story were no more bizarre than was many a spy trick played by Germany upon her foes. Spies were bound to be good actors. And this lantern-jawed fellow might possibly be a character actor of high ability. Colonel von Scheurer sat for moment in silence, peering up at Cash from beneath a thatch of stiff-haired brows. Then he ordered the captain and the others to leave the dugout.

Alone with Wyble the colonel still maintained his pose of majestic surveillance. Then with no warning he spat forth the question, "*Wer bist du?*"

Not the best character actor unhung could have simulated the owlish ignorance in Cash's face. Not the shrewdest spy could have had time to mask a knowledge of German. And, as Colonel von Scheurer well knew, no spy who did not understand German would have been sent to enlist in the German Army.

The colonel at once was satisfied that the newcomer was not a spy. Yet, to make doubly certain of the recruit's willingness to serve against his own country, von Scheurer sought another test. Pulling toward him a scratch pad, he picked up a pencil from the table before him and proceeded to make a rapid sketch. When the sketch was complete he detached the top sheet and showed it to Cash. On it was drawn a rough likeness of the American flag.

"What is that?" he demanded.

"Old Glory," answered Cash, after a leisurely survey of the picture, adding in friendly patronage, "and not bad drawed, at that."

"It is the United States flag," pursued the colonel, "as you say. It is the national emblem of the country where you were born; the country you are renouncing, to become a subject of the All Highest."

"Meanin' God?" asked Cash.

He wanted to be sure of every step. While he did not at all know the meaning of *renounce,* yet his attendance at mountain camp-meeting revivals had given him a possible inkling as to what "All Highest" meant.

"What?" inquired the puzzled colonel, not catching his drift.

"The 'All Highest' is God, ain't it?" said Cash.

"It is His Imperial Majesty, the Kaiser," sharply retorted the scandalized colonel.

"Oh!" exclaimed Cash, much interested. "I see. In West Virginia we call him God. An' over in this neck of the woods your Dutch name for Him is Kaiser. What a ninny I am! I'd always had the idea the Kaiser was just a man, with somethin' the same sort of job as President Wilson's. But. . . ."

"This picture represents the flag of the United States," resumed the impatient von Scheurer, waiving the subject of theology for the point in hand. "You have renounced it. You have declared your wish to fight against it. Prove that. Prove it by tearing that sketch in two—and spitting upon it!"

"Hold on!" interposed Cash, speaking with tolerant kindness as to a somewhat stupid child. "Hold on, Cap! You got me wrong. Or maybe I didn't make it so very clear. I didn't ever say I wanted to fight Old Glory. All I said I wanted to do was to fight that crowd of smart alecks over yonder who jail me all the time an' won't let me fight in my own way. I've got nothin' against the old flag. Why, that there's the flag I was borned under! Me an' Pop an' Grandfather an' the whole lot of us—as far back as there was any America, I reckon. I don't go round wavin' it none. That ain't my way. But I sure ain't goin' to tear it up. And I ain't goin' to spit on it. I. . . ."

He checked himself. Not that he had no more to say, but because to his astonishment he found he was beginning to lose his temper. This phenomenon halted his speech and turned his wondering thoughts inward.

Cash could not understand his own strange surge of choler. He had not been aware of any special interest in the American flag. A little bunting representation of the Stars and Stripes—now faded close to whiteness—hung on the wall of his shack at home, where his grandmother, a rabid Unionist, had hung it nearly sixty years earlier, when West Virginia had refused to join the Confederacy. Every day of his life Cash had seen it there, had seen without noting or caring.

Camp Lee, too, had been ablaze with American flags. And after he had learned the rules as to the flag salute, Cash had never given the banners a second thought. The regimental flags, too, here in France, had seemed to him but a natural part of the army's equipment, and no more to be venerated than the twin bars on his captain's tunic.

Thus he could not in the very least account for the fiery flare of rebellion that gripped him at this ramrodlike Prussian's command to defile the emblem. Yet grip him it did. And it held him there, quivering and purple, the strange emotion waxing more and more overpoweringly potent at each passing fraction of a second. Dumb and shaking, he glowered down at the amused colonel.

Von Scheurer watched him placidly for a few moments; then with a short laugh he advanced the test. Reaching for the sheet of paper whereon he had sketched the flag, the colonel held it lightly between the fingers of his outstretched hands.

"It is really a very simple thing to do," he said carelessly, yet keeping a covert watch upon the mountaineer. "And it is a thing that every loyal German subject should rejoice to do. All I required was that you first tear the emblem in two and then spit upon it—as I do now."

But the colonel did not suit action to words. As his fingers tightened on the sheet of paper the dugout echoed to a low snarl that would have done credit to a Cumberland catamount. And with the snarl, six feet of lean and wiry bulk shot through the air across the narrow table that separated Cash from the colonel.

Von Scheurer with admirable presence of mind snatched his pistol from its temporary resting place in his lap. With the speed of the wind he seized the weapon. But with the speed of the whirlwind Cash Wyble was upon him, his clawlike fingers deep in the colonel's full throat, his hundred and sixty pounds of bone and gristle smiting von Scheurer on chest and shoulder.

Cash had literally risen in air and pounced on the Prussian. Under the impact von Scheurer's chair collapsed. Both men shot to earth, the colonel undermost and the pistol flying unheeded from his grasp. Over, too, went the table, and the electric light upon it. And the dugout was in pitch blackness.

There in the dark Cash Wyble deliriously tackled his prey, making queer and hideous little worrying sounds now and then far down in his throat, like a dog that mangles its meat. And there the sentry from the earthen passageway found them when he rushed in with an electric torch, and followed by a rabble of fellow soldiers.

Cash at sound of the running footsteps jumped to his feet. The man he had attacked was lying very still, in a crumpled and yet sprawling heap—in a posture never designed by nature.

With one wild sweep of his windmill arms Cash grabbed up the sheet of paper on which von Scheurer had made his life's last sketch. With a simultaneous sweep he

knocked the glass-bulbed torch from the sentinel, just as
a rifle or two were centering their aim toward him; and,
head down, he tore into the group of men who blocked
the dugout entrance.

Cash had a faintly conscious sense of dashing down one
passageway and up another, following by forestry instinct
the course he noted when he was led into the colonel's
presence. He collided with a sentinel; he butted another
from his flying path. He heard yells and shots—especially
shots. Once something hit him on the shoulder, whirling
him half round without breaking his stride. Again something hot whipped him across the cheek. And at last he
was out, under the foggy stars, with excited Germans firing
in his general direction and loosing off star shells.

Again instinct and scout skill came to the rescue as he
plunged into a bramble thicket and wriggled through long
grass on his heaving stomach.

An hour before dawn Cash Wyble was led before his
sleepy and unloving company commander. The returned
wanderer was caked with dirt and blood. His face was
scored by briers. Across one cheek ran the red wale of a
bullet. A very creditable flesh wound adorned his left
shoulder. His clothes were in ribbons.

Before the captain could frame the first of a thousand
scathing words, Cash broke out pantingly, "Stick me in the
hoosegow if you're a mind to, Cap! Stick me there for life.
Or wish me onto a kitchen-police job forever! I'm not
kickin'. It's coming to me, all right, after what I done.

"I get the drift of the whole thing now. I'm on to what it
means. It—it means Old Glory! It means—*this!*"

He stuck out one muddy hand wherein was clutched a
wad of scratch-pad paper.

Then the company commander did a thing that stamped
him as a genius. Instead of administering the planned re-

buke and following it by sending the wretch to the guard-house, he began to ask questions.

"What do you make of it all?" dazedly queried the captain of Top Sergeant Mahan, when Cash had been taken to the trench hospital to have his shoulder dressed.

"Well, sir," reported Mahan meditatively, "for one thing, I take it, we've got a new soldier in the company. A soldier, not a varmint. For another thing, I take it, Uncle Sam's got a new American on his list of nephews. And—and, unless I'm wrong, Kaiser Bill is short one crackajack sniper and one perfectly good Prussian colonel, too. War's a funny thing, sir."

Courage

BY BRASSIL FITZGERALD

When they were youngsters of ten and twelve, the Sprague boys used to walk home alone after Sunday evening services. Peter was the elder, a stocky, unimaginative child, dark-skinned and awkward. Davy had nice features. He was fair like his mother's people.

As they neared the foot of Pride's Hill, Peter would take his brother's hand. Davy was afraid. That was on account of the old Baptist cemetery. The stones gleamed, and there were noises in the underbrush that fringed the road. As they topped the rise, the younger boy would draw away a little, and start chattering again.

Even in those days Peter had understood. Davy was different; things bothered him more. But he was smart, smarter than any of the others in the Pine Street school;

and he could talk to people, even to strangers, when Peter could only mutter unhappily.

When the war came, it was inevitable that the Sprague boys should be among the first from Braintree to go. A Sprague had followed Ethan Allen down from the hills. There were the many Decoration Days when they had stood very straight and silent beside their mother, while the Grand Army bugler sounded taps. It was in the Sprague blood.

Davy enlisted in Boston, on his way home from his freshman year at Tufts. Two weeks later, when he left to report for duty, Peter went with him.

It was September. The transport was rocking to the first long swells of the outer harbor. The brothers stood by the rail, watching their convoy nose out ahead. Somewhere in the distance behind them the fog was blurring out the ragged Hoboken water front.

David turned a shoulder against the gray shifting surfaces. "The old man has it in for me, I guess," he said suddenly, an apologetic note in his voice. He was looking at his brother's chevroned sleeve.

Peter watched a smudge of smoke on the horizon. "You'll be on the next list, Davy," he said awkwardly.

They were silent then. David was wondering what it would be like—over there. How long it would be. Peter was thinking of his brother. He wasn't sure—

Beneath their feet the great shafts plunged and recoiled —pushing them steadily, relentlessly, toward the unknown.

It was December. The third battalion had halted along the road beyond Ménil-la-Tour. At eight that night the division would take over a sector from the French. The men had done twelve muddy miles since noon, and they were profanely tired.

The rain had ceased falling and the sky was drawing away, cold and hard. A heavy rumbling came and went among the hills up ahead. A gray-blue camion lumbered by. Its bearded chauffeur dexterously caught a cigarette and grinned his thanks. The poplars dripped.

Sergeant Sprague, working down the line, reached his brother's squad. Davy was sitting on his unslung pack, a little withdrawn from the others. Peter noticed that as he squatted down beside him.

"How are the feet, Davy?"

"They're sore, Pete. Got any water?"

"Plenty." He reached for his canteen.

As he took the canteen back, he paused, his fingers on its cover. Out of the distance had come a purring noise—high up. A soft purr with a recurring throb in it. The men grew silent. The noise came louder and louder. Far up in the sky, somewhat off to the right, a tiny black insect was sailing slowly toward them.

"He's looking for the road," remarked Pete. Slipping the canteen back in his belt he snapped-to the felt covers. The word was passed along to cut out the cigarettes and lie flat.

The Boche plane was droning almost directly overhead. The men lay still. The plane swooped down toward the road. A bomb struck in the field behind them; the explosion beat on them—the Boche had passed over.

A voice came from the next squad, "Missed, you, you . . . !" A tense suppressed laugh. The Boche came circling back again. The drone of his engine grew louder and louder. It would be close this time. Davy's hand came into Pete's line of vision. It was very still—the hand. Then slowly, spasmodically, it twitched. It twitched as a shot rabbit twitches—convulsively. He was aware suddenly of a fear that had been with him from the beginning. Davy couldn't stand it. He was different. He wished to God the war would end—soon.

A flash, and the crash came. On the other side of the road a bit of iron rang on a helmet.

The plane didn't return. It hummed off toward Ménil-la-Tour. The men sat up and followed it with jeering comments. Davy clambered to his feet, laughing unsteadily.

Sprague grew leisurely awake. There was a patch of sunlight on the dugout floor. That meant afternoon. He had a vague memory of noise, heavy muffled sounds. He had slept since daylight. It was quiet outside. It had been a quiet two weeks. By this time tomorrow they would be back in reserve. The first battalion would be in to relieve them by dawn. He heard someone passing outside; the creak of heavy boots on the duckboards. Fritz had been lying low. It was a bad sign, that. Well—they'd be out tomorrow. He'd speak to the captain then about Davy. It was nothing to be ashamed of. Davy was sick. His nerves were screwed tight—to the breaking point. They could see for themselves.

He sat up and reached for his shoes, but the image of his brother's white face, the tense look of his eyes, persisted. Only one more day. The bags at the head of the stairs pushed in. It was Sergeant Ferber.

"Sleep through the row?" he grunted, pushing back his helmet.

"I heard something."

"They threw some Berthas over—knocked in a piece of the support trench."

Pete swung off his bunk and began winding on his spirals. Ferber stood watching him.

"Your brother's out of luck."

Sprague straightened up and waited—tense.

"He sneaked off post five when the fuss started. They picked him up crying like a kid."

It had come.

Sprague drew a quick sharp breath and bent over his leggings, his back to Ferber. He tucked in the tape ends and turned. "The kid's all in—he's sick," he said quietly.

Ferber spat his disgust. "He will be when they get through with him," he remarked judicially.

Sprague's eyes flamed. Then, without speaking, he went past Ferber to the stairs.

The sky was blue overhead. The guns were quiet, oppressively quiet. There was a soft thud above him. A little sand scattered down. Davy—Davy!

The lantern at Captain Doane's elbow flared and smoked. The shadow on the wall behind him bulked grotesquely. He gave no sign. Sprague spoke with an effort, a sense of futility dragging down his words. When he had done, the officer raised his eyes. He looked past Sprague.

"The court can consider his physical condition. That's not up to me," he said wearily.

Sprague's voice was steady. "Will you recommend clemency, sir?"

"I can't, Sprague. When your brother crawled off his post, he endangered the whole battalion. I can't let any feeling for you—"

There was more; something about justice and Pete's own record. The words blurred together. It didn't matter. Davy would be put under guard in the morning when they started out. They wouldn't shoot him—it would be Leavenworth. The *Concord Times* would have it. Jim Wetherby would bring the paper out to his mother.

The phone stuttered. As Doane reached for the set, Sprague saluted stiffly and turned away.

He was passing out of the orderlies' room when someone grabbed his elbow. "Are you deaf, Sarge? The old man wants you back."

The captain was waiting, drumming nervously on the table. "Price is on number nine. He thinks they've sneaked in and set up a machine gun off to his left."

As Pete listened, his brother's face grew indistinct. The ground sloped off to the left of number nine.

"They could get the support trench from that position, sir."

The captain jerked forward, scowling. "If they've got that support trench covered they've got wind we're going to be relieved. They're going to strafe us when we start out." He paused, and then went on grimly, "You know the men. Send someone out to look it over. If the Boches are there, we'll hold up the movement and shell them out in the morning."

A sense of relief—of escape—flashed on him. It would be a way out. Doane was waiting—giving him his chance.

A way out—for him. He stood silent.

The captain stirred impatiently. "Well? Tell the man who goes we'll make him if he gets back. That's all, Sergeant."

Sprague wormed his way through the narrow connecting ditch to number nine post. A fine rain was beginning to fall. The night was black and warm. Price pointed through the dark. Crouching together, they waited till a flare light shot up.

"Off to your left," whispered Price, "there's a shell hole. You can't see nothing, but there's a couple of Heinies in there with a machine gun, or I'll—"

"All right, Price. I'll send someone out to look it over. Don't open up if you hear us. I'll go part way myself."

Price cursed fervently under his breath. His whisper followed Sprague. "There's a ticket west waiting for the bird that goes."

Sprague knew it.

Davy lay crouched, his face to the wall. At the touch of his brother's hand he shivered and turned to stare up at him hopelessly. He tried to smile. His lips twitched.

Pete's face was granite. "Davy, get your shoes on. The C. O. wants you."

The members of Davy's squad were rolled in their blankets on the dugout floor. They had drawn away from his corner. One of them stirred in his sleep, but he didn't wake. Davy groped for his boots and stumbled after his brother.

In the trench outside, Pete gripped his shoulder. "You've got to get out and get out quick. They're going to line you up in the morning."

His brother's fingers clutched at his blouse. "My God, Pete! They wouldn't do that!"

"They've got to on account of the others." He put his arms around the boy and held him close. Then gently he broke the grasp of his fingers. "You're going over to the Boches, Davy. They will ship you back to a prison camp. After this thing is over, people won't remember."

He was glad of the darkness.

"I can't, Pete." There was nothing left but fear.

"It's your only chance. Sure you can. Come."

The boy shrank back.

"It's that or the firing squad, Davy."

A moment later they were on their faces, crawling beneath the wire. Out by number nine post. He could hear Davy breathing—quick forced gasps. Groping, he reached and found his hand. They crept on. Out past the vague hump that was number nine post. Five—ten yards beyond. A flare went up, and before the light failed he had aligned the suspected crater.

Drawing close, he whispered, "I've got to go back now, Davy. Keep straight on till you strike a shell hole, twenty-five yards out. Crawl in there till it starts to get light and then go over."

He drew swiftly back before Davy could hesitate, lest he refuse to go on. He could still get him back. He dug his fingers into the earth. The silence pushed down on him—it was too late now. The seconds hung back.

A roar shattered the night. The waiting Boche had swung his gun on the black smudge that had crept too near. A sharp staccato of shots. The silence settled down again. Sprague crept back under the wire. His lips were bleeding.

Captain Doane looked up anxiously. "Well, Sprague?"

"There's a machine gun there, sir. Thirty yards off post nine." There was a note of exhaustion in his voice. "He opened up and got our man."

Doane fumbled for his pipe. Their eyes met. "Who went, Sergeant?"

Pete lifted a suffering face. "Private Sprague, sir," he said proudly. Then his voice went flat. "Your lantern's smoking, sir. I'll send Webber in."

He stopped in the orderlies' room, and then went back to his brother's dugout—to gather up Davy's things. They would send them back to his mother.

Unknown

BY HARFORD POWEL, JR.

This is a story of Armistice Day. But it has nothing to do
with the rejoicings that went on, in every city in America
and in the whole world, when the great news came that the
war was over. I want to tell you of a boy who went to the
war—a boy named Michael Huss.

I find that I must begin with his uncle, who had been
christened Simi Hussinecz in the old country, but who
was called a bohunk in America, and therefore shortened
his name to Sim Huss. Uncle Sim did not like to be called
a bohunk. He was so grateful to America for having given

him a living, and he was so proud of his citizenship, that
he wanted to be known as an American.

"In America," he often said, "a man can have *anything!*"

Uncle Sim Huss began his life in this country with a
pick and shovel, digging ditches in Hoboken, New Jersey.
He saved his money, went west, and bought a little farm.
Then he opened a small general store, and when it began
to meet expenses he gave the farm to his oldest son, who
enlarged and improved it.

Uncle Sim's store was small, and dark, and not very
clean; but it was really the beginning of the town in which
he lived, and it gave Uncle Sim so much to do that in old
age he employed his nephew Michael as clerk.

"You are slow!" he said to the boy. "You don't hustle.
You have no future—no future at all."

Michael was an orphan. His father was Uncle Sim's
youngest brother, and he had died when Michael was a
baby. Then Uncle Sim and his wife, Aunt Natalia, took
Michael into their home and saw to his schooling. As Michael grew up, all his other uncles and aunts left home,
and bettered themselves. Uncle Sim did not complain. He
intended to stay always with the little store that had
brought him his wealth—that little fortune of a few thousand dollars which he had made. Uncle Sim was a pioneer.
In other clothes he would have looked like a Pilgrim father; he had a piercing eye, and a long white beard, but
he was crippled and bent and wore clothes that hardly
could be described—the ghost of a long black coat, the
phantoms of a pair of spring-sided shoes.

He loved America, and summed up his love in six words:
"Meat on the table every day."

Michael paid no attention to this frequently repeated
remark. His uncle rebuked him. "Do you know what we

had to eat in the old country? Food not good enough for the pigs here."

Michael was not impressed. He would have sat down without emotion to a Serbian peasant's dinner of turnips; he ate his Uncle Sim's cheap cuts of meat with equal calm. He was too calm. There was fire in Uncle Sim's make-up, but none showed itself in Michael.

He went through the long, slow days in the store so dumbly that he did not seem to know what they were all about. As a child in school, he was the same. Lessons meant little to him and games still less. As he moved slowly from grade to grade, he found only a few children of his own race. He was not persecuted by the boys of other races. They merely left him alone. There was one little girl named Ida in school, and sometimes Michael Huss and Ida were shunted off to one side of the playground; then they stood and talked to one another a little, and Ida asked Michael why he didn't take part in the games with the other boys.

Even when he was sixteen, and began to give all his time to helping Uncle Sim in the store, Michael had made no other friends at all. He used to wish, dumbly, that he had a home of his own. Uncle Sim and Aunt Natalia were kind to him, but they were not like a real father and mother. Michael thought he would like to be married, and have a store of his own, or else a farm. He could not make up his slow mind as to which of them he really wanted, a store or a farm.

"How did you get this store?" he asked Uncle Sim.

"My wife helped me."

There was no comfort for Michael in this explanation. He could not know that pioneers attain their rewards only because they dare to try for them. Uncle Sim had taken a great plunge when he broke away from the European town of Prague and came to America, a barefooted and penniless immigrant. His later plunges had not been so hard. He had become an American citizen. He noticed that native-born Americans are not common laborers, but own farms and stores. Therefore Uncle Sim had skimped and saved, until he too owned a farm and a store. But Michael was not capable of moving so directly, on such a straight line. He went dumbly and glumly through the days. He had only two remarks for the store's customers: "I'm sorry, but we're just out of it," and "What else today, lady?"

These are not remarks which improve business. Uncle Sim used to crowd in, whenever he could, between Michael and the customer. Uncle Sim's earnestness often saved a sale when Michael's stupidity or indifference threatened to wreck it.

On the evening of Michael's twenty-first birthday Uncle Sim gave him a pearl-handled nail file and a lecture.

"In America, what do we have? Meat on the table every day! Sleep warm every night! I am a poor man in America, but the people around Prague would call me rich. Thank God, I came to this country. In America, a man can have *anything.*"

"I want more money," said Michael without warning.

"And for what?" answered Uncle Sim. "You are asleep all the time. You drive customers away. You have no future—no future at all."

He waggled his beard and waved his arms so fiercely that Michael subsided. But the old man had fallen in love with his own words. He kept repeating them. "You have no future," he said.

Michael began to worry about this possibility. It seemed to him that he was caught in a trap. His uncle paid him wages, but most of the money went back to his uncle for board and lodging. Michael went out and asked the price of meals and rooms elsewhere. He found that his uncle was charging less than half the price of the cheapest boarding-house in town. The rest of Michael's money went for clothes—cheap clothes that never fitted him—and for other necessary expenses. He spent nothing on pleasure, for he had no pleasures. But he was thinking, in his dull way. One evening he said that the store ought to get a horse and wagon, and deliver packages.

"The new stores in town deliver goods. Why not our store?"

"Since when is it our store?" demanded Uncle Sim, and the subject dropped. Michael was either too frightened or too indifferent to bring it up again. He continued to shuffle around, in his dumb, heavy-footed way. He spoke thickly, as if he had an impediment. But he spoke so seldom that it hardly mattered.

One morning he permanently offended Mrs. Tim Morrissey, the star customer of the store. She was an impulsive, good-hearted woman, the wife of the chief of police. On this occasion, she tried to return a badly soiled shirt-waist, and Michael refused to accept it.

"You made it all dirty," he said. "We couldn't give you credit. No."

Mrs. Morrissey blazed at him, all her good nature turned to wrath. "It was dirty when I bought it!" she cried. "*Your hands*—look at them. *Your shelves*—I can write my name in the dust on them. Look!"

But Michael was shuffling away toward the back of the store. Uncle Sim came quickly forward, but he was too late. Mrs. Morrissey sailed out, quivering with rage throughout her vast bulk, and exclaiming that she would take her trade to Rosebloom's. Uncle Sim glared at Michael.

"I was right," said the boy. "She would make a habit of returning dirty goods in the future."

"Forget the goods," shouted Uncle Sim. "It's *you* that have no future—no future at all."

This was the seven-thousandth time, probably, that he had used these words. But seven thousand affirmatives do not necessarily make a fact. Uncle Sim was wrong. Michael had the most amazing future that has come to any American of his age.

He would have left the store, if he could. But he had no place to go. He was afraid to ask a farmer for a job, afraid of garages and big stores, afraid of any city bigger than his own. And he knew that his uncle and aunt loved him in their own fashion. He was thin, but he was getting good food. He was a pale, underdeveloped young fellow, but he was never sick. What eventually took him out of the store was not sickness, or even his inability to be a good clerk. He was blasted out of the store by a law of the United States.

The news came from Mrs. Morrissey's son, Patrick. Michael had no place to go in the evenings, so he usually lounged on the street corners before going to bed. In the towns unlucky enough to have no Y.M.C.A., or other good meeting place for young men, they must lounge on street corners. But there is a difference in the desirability of these corners. Michael usually chose a dark and obscure corner near the store. He had been at school with Patrick, but Patrick had never spoken to him since.

Now Patrick came along the dark street and found Michael standing alone near the corner. "Been looking for you, Mike," he said. "How are you going to like being a soldier?"

Michael blinked. "I am not going to be," he said slowly. "I am not going to enlist. I am not interested."

"Is that so?" asked Patrick, sharply. "Don't you ever read the papers?"

"I'm too busy."

"Well, watch your step," said Patrick. "There's been a new law passed. If you are between twenty-one and thirty-one years old, you'll have to join the army whether you like it or not. That's the law."

Michael was still blinking. He said nothing.

"Get on to yourself," added Patrick. "If you don't register in the draft, you will be arrested."

Michael had a dread of that last word. He had seen the recruiting posters, of course. He knew that America was at war.

He meditated darkly and silently for an hour, and then took the news to his uncle. Uncle Sim had been well acquainted with compulsory military service in his youth. "You will have to go," he said.

For the first time in his life, Michael went on the following day to see Ida. He found her washing clothes at her father's home. She looked at Michael with new interest; there was a smouldering fire in her dark eyes. She gave him a great deal of information about the draft, and about ways of getting exempted. Flat feet, bad eyesight, bad hearing, heart trouble—there were apparently any number of things that would disqualify a man from service.

"But I'm well," said Michael, stubbornly.

"I thought your feet might be cold," said Ida.

He looked at her dumbly. "My feet are all right," he said. "I did not know this country wanted me. Of course I will go—now, today, before they come and grab me."

Ida smiled. "You want to be a soldier? You want to go and fight?"

Michael told her, without preliminaries of any kind, and in his curious, halting, flat tone of voice, that he wanted nothing of the kind—he wanted to marry her, to have a store of his own, and live in rooms over it, and have children. It was the strangest declaration of its kind that you can imagine. Michael spoke exactly as if he were telling her that he wanted her to do his aunt's washing.

"I never knew what I wanted before," said Michael, truthfully.

"I believe you," said the girl. "All right—tell them you have heart trouble."

But Michael was shaking his head, stubbornly, like a bull. "The country needs me," he said. "After the war— then we'll see, maybe. Just now I am going to enlist."

She watched his little, stooping figure as he shuffled away toward the street. She thought of asking him to say good-by in more seemly fashion. But she was not emotional, any more than he was. She returned to her washing.

Michael plodded downtown to the recruiting office and found it closed. He beat on the door, and it was opened by a sergeant—a burly regular-army sergeant, who had been cording up some boxes in preparation for going away.

"Too late, buddy," he said. "You'll have to register, now."

"But I want to go in the army right away," said Michael. "Will it be the same thing, to register?"

"You'll get action," replied the sergeant.

Michael was comforted. To his uncle he seemed much wider awake during the days that followed.

"War is one big waste," said the old man. "But I wish I could go with you, little Michael. I wish I could pay America part of the debt I owe."

On June 5 Michael went to register.

It was a drab event. Men who had expected it to be fine and inspiring were disappointed as badly as were men who had predicted there would be riots. Michael wrote his name in a book in a barbershop and received a card which read:

REGISTRATION CERTIFICATE   No. 78

To whom it may concern, Greetings:

THESE PRESENTS ATTEST that in accordance with the Proclamation of the President of the United States, and in compliance with law,

Michael Huss

has submitted himself to registration and has by me been duly registered this 5th day of June, 1917.

Charles C. Rubino
Registrar

Michael put his card in his pocket, returned to the store, and worked all day as usual. But in the evening he went to Ida's house and told her that he had enlisted in the draft. And now, curiously, she looked at him with shining eyes, and told him that he would now be given a number, and that this number would be drawn by lot in Washington. On the day when Michael's number was drawn, she started to knit a sleeveless sweater for him, and she gave him six handkerchiefs with his initial on them.

Michael carried one in his breast pocket when he went up for his medical examination. He stripped in a large, crowded room, leaving his clothes on a chair at one side. When he went back, his handkerchief was gone, and so was his money.

Patrick Morrissey was there too, arguing with a doctor who had said that his feet were flat. "I'm a ballplayer," said

Patrick. "I'm fast enough to play ball—just give me a gun, and I'll show you how many of the enemy I can catch."

He was refused, however. He went out with his head hanging; several weeks later another doctor accepted him.

There were many others like Michael in the room; fine-looking boys, who went through the examination with their heads up and were glad to be passed; and many others with some glaring physical defect that could have been corrected when they were younger. And there were others, a sullen and slanting-eyed minority, who tried hard to fail.

But the doctors had found ways of exposing all such cowardly pretenses. One doctor had a slacker in front of him, pretending deafness in one ear. The man put his finger in the other ear, and shook his head hopelessly when the physician spoke to him. The test went on for some time.

"All right," said the doctor. "We can't accept you. You are stone-deaf in one ear." And then he added, very softly, "Take your hand down."

Instantly the man's hand dropped to his side.

But such skulkers were few, and the men were behaving just as they did when they registered. Waiting their turn, they laughed and joked, and wondered when they would go over the top. A man in line behind Michael whistled and hummed a variety of little songs like this:

Good-by, Dolly, I must leave you,
  Though it breaks my heart to go;
Something tells me I am needed
  At the front to face the foe. . . .

Then a doctor beckoned to Michael, and he shuffled out; a pale, thin, slab-sided little figure, with no expression whatever on his face. The doctor went over him rapidly, listening to his heart, and prodding him sharply in various tender places.

"You're sound," he said. "But what have you been doing to cripple your feet? Let's see your shoes."

Michael padded over and brought his shoes.

"What do you think your toes are *for?*" asked the doctor, gruffly. "Those toothpick shoes would have crippled you. But you're lucky. The army shoes will do wonders for your arches, and your bunions."

Michael didn't understand. But he discovered, a month later, that the well-fitting army boots issued to him by a camp quartermaster were the first he had ever worn in which he could wriggle his toes. Apart from this, he found no comfort in any detail of his equipment. It did not fit his lopsided frame.

"You are so unstylish!" said Ida, when she saw him on leave of absence from the training camp. Michael's breeches sagged at the waist; his canvas leggings sprawled down over the square-tipped shoes—his blouse was too tight in the back and far too loose across his chest. Ida sent him upstairs to her father's room. He wrapped an old raincoat around himself and came down with his uniform over his arm. Ida and her mother strove with needle and sewing machine to make it presentable. They ripped it apart and resewed it. But the final effect was not stylish at all.

Back at the training camp, Michael went through endless routine. They drilled him for hours every day, including setting-up exercises conducted by a sergeant with a steely, light-blue eye.

This was the same man who had whistled during the medical examination. He had served two hitches in the old army; and, although he wasn't thirty-one, he had the wrinkled, dried face of a man of fifty. Sergeant Flaherty became the terror of Michael's existence.

"Leaning r-rest in six counts!"

Michael, at this command, prostrated himself on the palms of his hands and his boot tips. His stomach rested on the ground. Then he tried to push himself up with his hands. He could do it once. Then his flabby triceps muscles failed to lift him. He lay prone, like a squashed beetle.

The sergeant came over and brooded menacingly. He threatened in a hoarse, alarming whisper to stir Michael with the toe of his boot. Sergeant Flaherty could perform any exercise indefinitely; his body was rubber and whipcord. Michael's body was mushy. In his leanness there was no strength. A drill sergeant is likely to pick out one man as a horrible example, and remember him from day to day, and ride him unmercifully. Sergeant Flaherty rode Michael.

Michael continued dutifully to attempt the setting-up drill. He never achieved success, and he never learned to *look* as if he were successful. The steely-blue eye penetrated into his marrow. After what seemed an eternity in the training camp the division was ordered overseas.

By this time, Michael was a trifle more muscular than he had been. A few months in camp will not put perfect strength and suppleness into a boy who has neither. But it helps. And Michael had been assigned to a duty in which strength and suppleness were not necessary. He was a K.P.

Except during the Kitchen Police duty, he was totally inconspicuous. His uniform, despite Ida's best efforts, was the worst fitting of all the uniforms in his squad. His blouse, though it looked a little better in front, rose up and wrinkled strangely in the rear.

The journey to France was long and dull. Michael was not afraid of periscopes. Kitchen Police duty aboard the transport filled his time completely—it was merely a little harder and hotter than K.P. duty ashore. Landed, the division went into training quarters. As far as Michael was concerned, this training made no difference. He fluked on bayonet drill as completely as he had fluked on other drill.

Further eternities passed. Some regiments went up to the line. Michael remained. By the middle of 1918 he was firmly and permanently attached to a headquarters company which performed tedious duties in a small French town.

Even Michael, who neither saw nor understood very much, could not help noticing that this French town was much poorer than the town in America from which he came. The people did not have meat on the table every day. He missed the movies. He saw no stores as large as the store of Uncle Sim. He was nowhere near the front and never heard a shot fired except in practice. He was merely in a little town on the other side of France.

The whole war, as far as he was concerned, was a chore. He peeled potatoes and turned the handle of the meat chopper. Before inspections, he was taught to take the chopper apart and clean its wormlike inside until it shone like silver.

He received several letters from Uncle Sim. They were not very interesting. But they made Michael regret that he was not at home. He would have liked even his old opportunities to stand alone on dark street corners. Perhaps Patrick Morrissey would let him stand on the brighter corners, when the war was over. He wrote twice to Ida, and she sent him a picture postcard. In the space marked "correspondence here" she told him that Uncle Sim was doing an improved business.

It was all safe, slow, and dull. It remained so, even after he was transferred to another headquarters company nearer the front. The commanding officer was a lieutenant named Johnson. And there was a familiar face in the new company. Sergeant Flaherty was there. He remembered Michael.

The principal duty of the company was to police the ground around headquarters, and up to the quarters of troops who were in support of the line. They cleaned and disinfected all sorts of unpleasant things. Michael acquired a strong chemical odor. He walked miles every day through desolate fields—fields over which battles had been fought in the early years of the war.

Sergeant Flaherty saw to it that Michael did the dirtiest work. He climbed down into pits and spread around fresh earth which was shoveled to him from overhead. He was powdered thickly with chloride of lime.

Sometimes a faint rumbling sound, like a distant thunderstorm, came from the horizon in the east. Michael was told that this was artillery, thirty miles away.

"And you'll never be nearer to it," said Flaherty, with a scowl. "You're too valuable here. There's the corpse of a horse out behind the mayor's house. Run out there, Michael, and disinfect."

Michael stolidly approached the white-eyed horror, from which a flock of birds fluttered up into the air. He doused it with disinfectants and returned for further orders.

Lieutenant Johnson wore horn-rimmed glasses. He whistled all day. He had only one tune—a bad tune called "Bonbon Buddy, the Chocolate Drop." There were no old soldiers in his command, except Sergeant Flaherty; but Lieutenant Johnson was not an experienced soldier himself. He was merely cleaning up behind advancing troops; as they advanced, his company advanced closer in their rear.

On October 20, 1918, at half past three in the afternoon, the lieutenant and the sergeant led a platoon along a rough road through a wood. It was an ugly little wood, full of scraggly trees and low bushes. There were unmistakable signs that it had been fought through very recently.

The autumn twilight was setting in, and it was so dark in the wood that it was not the lieutenant's fault that he took a wrong turn. He marched for an hour and did not come to the village at which he was to report.

The men in Michael's squad marched in single column. Michael walked last. The man in front of him had a mandolin strapped to his back. But he supplied no music. The only music came from the officer's lips:

"Bonbon Buddy, the Chocolate Drop,
The Chocolate Drop, that's me!"

Sergeant Flaherty walked slightly in the rear of the lieutenant. The man with the mandolin talked a good deal. "Wish the loot would get a new record," he said. "That fool tune makes me tired."

A shot cracked out on the left. "Bonbon Buddy" died away in a choking gurgle as the bullet passed through the lieutenant's throat. The wood was suddenly full of gray uniforms. Gray-clad figures of the enemy sprang up like ghosts in the twilight. They were shooting fast.

Flaherty turned, with a mighty leap of his rubber and whipcord body. He saw his men straggling along in column. "As skirmishers," he roared. "March."

He died, pistol in hand, in his tracks. The men made a hasty, confused effort to obey his command. They deployed raggedly. Michael ran to his right, tripped over a root, and fell sprawling into a mass of leaves and twigs— the bushy top of a fallen tree.

He lay unseen in this cover, and heard the word *surrender* shouted just ahead of him. The men near Michael

had dived into the bushes. One or two of them fired at
random, and then the enemy bayonets started to seek them
out.

Michael lay close and began to realize the strange thing
which had happened. He had been far from the war. But
now the war was here. These men in gray were the enemy.
Lieutenant Johnson had marched straight into them, and
they had killed him. They were trying to kill all the other
Americans.

A surge of fury swept through Michael. He knew suddenly why he was in France. All his old timidity flooded
away from him. For the first time in his life he felt thoroughly clear-headed and awake. Killing Americans, were
they? Shooting and stabbing his friends, men who had
slept with him, worked with him, done all kinds of tasks
with him! Michael peered out through the heavy branches.
He was safe there. He would not be found. The enemy
were walking through the wood in front of him, looking
for easy victims.

But Michael knew what he would do. He would fight!
He would avenge the death of so many of his companions;
and perhaps the noise would bring up another American
company, who would overcome the enemy.

He got onto his knees, cocked his pistol, and stood up.
The leafy branches cascaded off his back. He knew it
meant death to be seen, but he did not care. One spasm of
deadly fear ran through him. It passed, and he walked out.

The setting sun struck squarely in his eyes, and he
blinked, looking for the enemy. He heard a voice before he
saw them in the glare. "Keep your hands up!" ordered the
voice. "Surrender."

"No!" shouted Michael, and charged.

His charge was a clumsy, stumbling trod, and many bullets were aimed at him before he had taken three steps.

The enemy officer shot him as coolly as if Michael had been a charging boar. But the shot passed through his shoulder, and he kept his feet. Other shots rang out. Still Michael, lurching from the impact of many bullets, kept staggering forward. Something held him up till he neared the officer; it may have been luck or chance, but I think it was force of will. He got there, and drove the muzzle of his pistol against the smooth gray cloth over the officer's chest, and fired one shot.

Then he went to his knees. His body was all one mass of pain, but his eyes were wide-open. He fired his remaining six shots, left and right. Then he crashed forward on his face.

There were more shots fired during this episode than had been fired before. An American company, going into position on the right, heard them and came up at a run. They drove the enemy detachment out of the wood. And then they found Michael lying there dead, with the dead officer in front of him, and other dead men, left and right.

"By heaven," said the American captain who led this company, "it looks to me as if that little man had charged the whole gang, singlehanded!"

"That's what he did," answered a survivor of Michael's squad. "I saw him do it myself. He was a bohunk, too."

The American captain took off his helmet.

"He was a brave man," he answered. "Do something like that yourself, before you call *him* names."

They buried Michael, temporarily, where he lay.

For those whose habit it is to doubt, this story has already ended. But I believe that the rest of us may have one more glimpse of Michael, the boy who had no future at all.

In that long minute under the fallen tree he lived his

whole life, and was actually born again, both as an American and a man. And in the few crowded seconds that followed he filled his life with achievement; by his gallant and utterly hopeless combat with enemies who surrounded him, he gave warning that his fellow Americans were in peril, and he saved many of them. A life may be short or long. What matters at the end is the measure of accomplishment it holds. Michael was tried and not found wanting in that moment; he achieved his destiny *then*.

There is no system, whether in peace or in war, that can keep *everything* from going wrong. Michael should have worn an identification disc. One was given to him, but he had lost it many months before. There might have been papers in his pocket, other things by which he could be recognized. But there were none. He was an unknown soldier, when his body was removed from its temporary grave. And I believe that when, among all the other unknown men, it was time to select one for eternal honor as the Unknown Soldier of the United States, Michael Huss may have been the man. For, in the great and fearless and conglomerate army of our boys who went to France, there were thousands of boys like Michael—boys who had not thought deeply about their love of America, but who were not found wanting when the great adventure came. The choice was made at last by a sergeant, who designated one coffin at random out of a row of unmarked coffins, so that nobody could ever tell on whom the honor fell. But if, as I believe, it fell upon this man, there could be no man to begrudge it to him among all the men who did come home.

Perhaps you were in the city of Washington, when the Unknown Soldier was buried.

There was a long procession that moved out toward Arlington Cemetery. There were great multitudes of spectators, standing with heads bared while a coffin was reverently brought to a glorious tomb. Behind and above this vast assembly that listened in solemn silence while the music rose and fell must have stood another and still larger audience—an invisible host. There were men in that unseen multitude who fought at Yorktown and Gettysburg and Palo Alto and the hill of San Juan. For this cemetery is the last earthly home of men who have worn their country's uniform. Sailors and soldiers, they stood unseen while the body of the Unknown Soldier was buried with such honors as have come before to no other American in history.

And if these men were there in spirit, I know that George Washington was there, and that Abraham Lincoln watched the burial with eyes that held both pity and pride; and I believe that somewhere near these two stood a shorter figure, still in olive-drab uniform—in the sagging breeches and the wrinkled blouse—the spirit of Michael Huss, and watched while the body of Michael Huss was lowered into its splendid grave.

The ceremony came to an end. Streetcars began to run again, newsboys shouted, typewriters clicked in offices, and machines rumbled in mills. There had been a hush over the whole nation while the Unknown Soldier was buried; such a hush as has never come before, may never come again, in our history.

Back at home in his rooms over the little store, Uncle Sim Huss sat down to supper with his wife. "I still wonder what became of our Michael," he said. "In America, a man can have *anything*."